To Andrea Ellis, Clifford Coulston and Natalie Evans

© Tom Slemen 2004

Edited by Claire Walker
Published by The Bluecoat Press, Liverpool
Book design by March Design, Liverpool
Printed by Universities Press, Belfast

ISBN 1 904438 23 7

Tom Slemen

HAUNTED
LIVERPOOL 10

The Bluecoat Press

CONTENTS

INTRODUCTION

Well, here we are. This is the tenth volume of the *Haunted Liverpool* series. Sometimes I find it hard to believe that ten of my books have gone by – plus *Haunted Cheshire, Haunted Wirral, Wicked Liverpool, Mysterious World*, and *Mysteries*. It has been great fun researching and writing all of the *Haunted Liverpool* books and I am working on a new series about Liverpool that will be out soon. I have so many people to thank, but the first person on that list is you, the reader. .

I have some of the most loyal readers in the north west, and unlike some people who become affected with over-inflated egos after writing a book, for me, I always find it a pleasure to oblige when someone asks me to sign a copy of *Haunted Liverpool*. The public is the paymaster, and deserves the utmost respect. The public has the control to make or break a budding writer, and in my case I have been so grateful for the kind people who have attended talks, queued at book signings, and taken time out to write to me about their own experiences, as well as listening to me when I have reeled off so many ghost stories on the radio. I would like to offer a big heartfelt thankyou to you all.

Then there are so many other people I have to thank for making *Haunted Liverpool* happen in the first place. There is my publisher, Colin Wilkinson, who took a big risk on an unknown writer, and of course Billy Butler, the man who gave me confidence when I first appeared on his radio show. I remember listening to Billy Butler on the radio before I ever met him, and he was ranting on about someone who had stolen a child's new bike, and I thought to myself, God, I'd hate to get into an argument with him! I never suspected that within a year I'd be appearing on his show each week, and watching him in action was an inspiration. Billy is always proud of his Liverpudlian roots, and never puts on a voice, whether he is talking to a visiting Hollywood film star, or the latest idol of the pop charts. His confidence was contagious in my case.

I feel indebted to another of my inspirations, Mr Rex Makin, a legendary man who I have interviewed on many occasions, including recent interviews with him while I have been conducting research for his memoirs. I'd say he is the most intelligent, witty and well-read gentleman I have ever met, and his knowledge of classical music – and human nature – is encyclopaedic. Whenever I have visited his abode, Professor Makin and his beautiful wife Shirley have always made me feel completely at home. I once discussed the Knowsley Hall murder case of 1952 with Rex, and remarked that there was no apparent motive for the shooting dead of two stately home employees, but Rex knew quite well just exactly what chain of events had led to the double tragedy, and astounded me with a story he will never allow into print. His insight and knowledge has been a true inspiration to my writing and research.

I also have to thank the stand-up comic and cult radio presenter Pete Price, who has given me hours of airtime on Magic 1548. Pete has plugged my talks and books for many years, and the only time we have crossed swords was when he intended to dabble with a ouija board live on air. Although Pete has one hundred per cent show business in his blood, and ran the Shakespeare Theatre for twelve years, he is also a very compassionate man who does a lot of work for charities such as Claire House.

I apologise to anyone I've forgotten to acknowledge. I still write about the paranormal in the *Merseymart* and *Star*, and at the time of writing, I have a column in the *Liverpool Echo* called Tales from the Past. I will also be appearing on the radio, relating spooky stories. I plan to continue writing books on the unusual and supernatural for as long as my readers want me to.

Tom Slemen
Liverpool

UNEXPLAINED MYSTERIES

THE STRANGER

This is an old tale of Edwardian Liverpool, which features a largely forgotten folklore character. One rainy and very humid Wednesday evening in July 1909, a stranger entered the Lady of the Lake public house, which once stood at Number 41 Brownlow Hill. The man wore a wide-brimmed floppy fedora, and a long, dark grey overcoat. The barman asked the man what he wanted and was told, "A glass of imperial stout".

Two uncouth and foul-mouthed regulars, Mick McTiernan and Eddy O'Brien, tried to engage the stranger in conversation; asking him where he was from and querying whether he was not hot wearing a fedora on such a warm summer night.

The man tried to ignore the two locals, but they were enjoying themselves and continued to mock his appearance. The stranger had a prominent, aquiline nose, small darting eyes, and swept-back eyebrows that met in the middle. He wore a distinguished dark Vandyke beard, and had long tapering fingers with well-kept but rather pointed nails.

"'Ere, mister. Are you deaf as mutton, or just plain iggirant?" asked McTiernan, getting uncomfortably close to the stranger's unresponsive face.

"Shut up, Mick," mumbled the barman, not wanting any sort of disturbance in his pub.

Then Mick's associate Eddy joined in and started criticising the new customer.

"Think we're below you, do you?" sneered Eddy and he prodded the man's shoulder with his index finger. It proved to be a big mistake.

The stranger whipped round his head to face Eddy and spat out a mouthful of imperial stout straight into his eyes. The barman was completely taken aback by the action, especially since the visitor hadn't even paid for the drink yet. Mick swung a punch, and the stranger jerked his head back with lightning reflexes, but Mick's fist caught the brim of his hat and sent it flying off the stranger's head, revealing a very unusual sight indeed. The man had long pointed ears, and small, hornlike appendages just above his eyebrows. His hairline was pointed too, dipping down in the middle of his forehead in a widow's peak. His eyes were unsynchronised, moving independently like those of a lizard as it tracks flies. The whole effect was very disturbing.

Naturally, the barman had witnessed numerous fights in all his years at the pub, but the two punches inflicted by the bizarre-looking stranger were, without a doubt, the most powerful he had ever seen. One lightning blow instantly knocked out Eddy O'Brien, and the other one sent his friend sailing across tables and landing in a crumpled heap at the other end of the room.

The startled customers looked on in fearful silence, not wanting to become embroiled with this creepy stranger who seemed to have superhuman powers. The most incredible part of this eventful evening was yet to take place. The stranger suddenly started to shriek with high-pitched laughter, then jumped clean over the bar, almost hitting his head on the ornate ceiling mouldings. People in the bar must have thought that the legendary Spring-Heeled Jack was paying a surprise visit, for no human could exercise such incredible acrobatic skills.

The ultra-athletic madman then proceeded to perform a succession of somersaults, he scuttled up walls and then started to hurl bottles and glasses at everybody. There was a mass exodus from the pub as drinkers fled to the doors and poured out on to Brownlow Hill. A few of the braver drinkers stayed behind to tackle the gymnastic troublemaker, but soon found themselves to be no match for his unearthly skills. The fiend stood on one man's shoulders, leapt on to a table, swung from a chandelier and then back-flipped out of the pub via the main doorway. He ran at an incredible speed up Ainsworth Street and soon vanished into a dark labyrinth of courts.

The drinkers gradually filed back into the Lady of the Lake pub avidly discussing the recent events. Inside the pub they found an old plasterer named Longfellow, sitting serenely in the corner of the bar with a knowing smile on his face. His glass of Irish whiskey was still intact. People asked the old man if the demonic mischief-maker had hurt him, and Mr Longfellow told them a strange tale.

He was calm as he answered the concerned onlookers. He related how he had seen the very same acrobatic madman at an old tavern in the Rainhill area, about twenty years ago. Some called him the 'Galosher Man' among other strange names, and said he was what was known as 'otherkin' – strange-looking people who are the offspring of human and supernatural creatures. Spring-Heeled Jack and other various bogeymen were otherkin, according to old Longfellow.

The Galosher Man – so called because of the strange boots he always wore – occasionally attempted to live among mankind by entering inns and even churches disguised as a human being, but he was usually soon exposed for what he was.

When the drinkers heard old Mr Longfellow's claims, they refused to venture outside the pub, just in case the Galosher Man was still lying in wait for them in the dark alleyways which criss-crossed the area. Apparently an unplanned lock-in ensued and the drinkers didn't leave until the sun was up!

THROUGH A GLASS DARKLY

The following tales are about strange incidents glimpsed through windows. At the old Adelphi Hotel, in late December 1901, a homesick travelling businessman named Frank Bertrand was sitting in his room one evening with the lights turned down low, mulling over the loneliness of his itinerant life with a glass of brandy in his hand. He gazed out of the open window. Frank was staring intently at two other windows across the road in Tobin Street. The bay window on the left framed a happy family scene. The father was playing an accordion in front of the blazing parlour fire, and his wife was singing, with her young son and daughter smiling at her feet. Garlands of holly and ivy decorated the walls and the whole scene was like something from a Christmas card.

Frank's heart sank with homesickness at the sight of this blissful scene of domesticity, and he tearfully longed to be back with his own family in Wolverhampton. He had promised his son that he would be home for Christmas, which was just three days away.

The window of the house next door to the happy family displayed a contrasting scene of loneliness and despair. By the light of a low gas jet, a man could be seen slumped over a table in a sparsely furnished room, with his face buried in his hands. Nearby, on the table, was a bottle of some spirit, and Frank presumed that the man had been trying to drink away some personal tragedy. Little did he know that the nature of that awful tragedy was soon to be revealed.

As Frank Bertrand speculated on the causes of the lonely man's grief, there was sudden cloudburst, followed by a relentless downpour of hail. As the pea-sized particles of ice showered the night-time street, lightning flashed high above the hotel and in the first flash of dazzling light, Frank glimpsed a white figure in the dark panes of the window facing his hotel room. In the upper room of the lonely man's house, stood a girl in a white nightgown, and smoke appeared to be pouring from a flickering flame at her chest!

Frank was immediately concerned and leaned out of the hotel room window to look a little closer. Squinting through the heavy hail and sleet, he tried to make his mind up; was the girl on fire, or was it a line-of-sight optical illusion caused by her holding a candle before her. No, he decided, the girl was definitely on fire, and she was staring at him with her mouth wide open, in a state of shocked horror.

Frank rushed out of his room and down to the foyer, where, wild-eyed, he caused quite a stir among the guests. He raced to the back of the hotel, and located the house on Tobin Street where he had seen the girl on fire. He hammered on the doorknocker and eventually the man he had seen sitting forlornly at the table answered. In a rush, Frank told him about the girl upstairs with her nightgown alight, but the man simply shook his head and stood there swaying.

"But I saw her ...!" screamed Frank.

"No, sir," he said in a slurred voice, and a strong aroma of whisky reached Frank's nostrils. The man then stepped aside, and said, "But come and see for yourself."

Frank walked into the hallway. The man closed the door behind him and then led him up the stairs in pitch darkness, knowing every step of the way. Frank stumbled on the flight of steep stairs, feeling his way, until the man reached a bedroom. A gas mantle was lit, and its faint luminosity revealed a small child's bed in an otherwise empty room. It had bare floorboards and smelt of damp. Through the grimy window, Frank could see his own hotel room across the street, but then the man pointed out something which was very peculiar and alarming.

"That is what you saw, sir," he said, pointing to the grimy window panes.

A faint, life-sized image of a girl of about ten or eleven years of age was somehow imprinted on the four panes of glass in the bedroom window. Her eyes were wide open with terror, as was her small O-shaped mouth. A black singed section of fabric was plainly visible where

11

a flame had seared the front of her nightgown, at the chest.

"Is ... is this some kind of ... of image on a kind of photographic plate?" Frank stammered, struggling to interpret the unearthly sight he was beholding.

"No, sir," said the man, in a deeply mournful voice. "This imprint of my little girl was caused by her being struck by lightning ten years ago."

"Lightning?" Frank muttered softly, instantly believing what the poor man was telling him.

When he inspected the image more closely he could even make out the individual strands of hair and the intense blueness of her wide-open eyes, all imprinted into the glass panes of the bedroom window.

"She always did the opposite of whatever I told her to do," said the man. "I told her to stay in bed that night, on account of the thunderstorm, but she would look out through the window. Somehow the bolt passed through the glass panes and struck her. She died more or less instantly, I reckon. Burnt a hole straight through her heart you see."

"You poor man!," said Frank, laying a hand on his arm, not knowing what else to say.

"People have offered me money for this window, but I'll never sell it. Terrible as it is, it's all I have to remember her by."

Frank Bertrand took one last look at the ghostly image of the girl in her final death throes in the murky window panes, then, deeply saddened, he returned to his hotel room. With a shudder he closed the window and drew the curtains, but could not help noticing, as he did so, that the man opposite was seated at the table once again with his head bowed – the picture of misery, a misery which he now fully understood.

There were a few more references to the 'ghost in the window' in Tobin Street, but when the old Adelphi was demolished to make way for the new hotel, the house with the apparition in its window panes was also knocked down. The busy demolition men may not have even noticed the terrible lightning photograph in the bright light of day as they smashed in the window frames.

~

Another window phantasm – and one I have heard of many times – concerns a certain house on Rathbone Road, which runs from the junction of Wellington Road, Wavertree High Street and Picton Road, to Edge Lane.

One winter evening, in the early 1970s, a teenager named Dan was travelling on a bus (probably the Number 60) from his home on Smithdown Road to his Aunt Mary's house in Stoneycroft. Dan was a police cadet based at Woolton, and often journeyed to his aunt's to tell her about the latest aspects of his training.

He sat on the top deck of the bus, and as it travelled up Rathbone Road, he idly scanned the softly illuminated ground floor and first floor windows of the terraced houses as the bus passed them by. As the bus reached a certain house on this road, Dan momentarily caught sight of a shocking scene. A bald man with his back to the window, had his right arm raised, and in his hand he held an axe. Before this man was a woman with a head of curly grey hair, and she too had her back towards the window. In the second it took for the bus to hurtle past, Dan gasped in revulsion and shock as he saw the man bring the axe-head down squarely on the back of the woman's head. In that brief instant of horror, he saw arterial blood spray from the woman's head as she simultaneously fell forwards from the blow.

Dan sprang up from his seat and turned to the only two other passengers on the top deck – a boy and girl of about sixteen, who were kissing one another on the back seat. They were obviously lost in each other's affection, and had not seen the terrible incident.

Dan dashed downstairs and told the driver to let him off at the next traffic lights. As the bus driver decelerated the vehicle, Dan blurted out to him what he had just seen, and the driver advised the young man to telephone the police. Dan mentioned that he was a police cadet, as if suggesting that he could cope with the situation on his own, upon which the driver, who obviously did not share his confidence, repeated his advice to call the police.

So, as soon as he had jumped off the bus, the youth ran to a telephone box and dialled 999. Fifteen minutes later, a police car pulled up at the same telephone box on Rathbone Road, but Dan was no longer there. He was on the other side of the road, foolishly making house-to-house inquiries of his own. He wasn't having much luck, not one of the people who had answered the door looked anything like the bald hatchet man.

The police soon gathered what was going on and they approached Dan, and tried to ascertain at which house he'd seen the alleged murder taking place. Dan was adamant that it was a specific house with parted red curtains, but when the police made inquiries there, they found no bloodstained aftermath of a murder or any bald man wielding an axe. Dan was virtually accused of inventing the whole incident and wasting police time. However, those who knew him at the Police Training College on Mather Avenue vouched for his honesty and integrity, saying that his only real fault was his over-enthusiasm for the job.

What the police did not know was that many other people had seen the 'phantom murder' of Rathbone Road, both before and after Dan's experience, and no one has been able to ascertain whose murder is actually being witnessed.

Around 1969, another upstairs bus passenger saw a bald man brutally smashing in the head of an elderly woman in the window of a house on Rathbone Road, and on this occasion it was doubly terrifying because the girl who witnessed it had an uncle who lived in the very house where she had glimpsed the blood-curdling assault.

She told her father what she had seen as soon as she reached her home in Old Swan, and he and his brother visited the house at once, only to find nothing amiss. There have been many more sightings of the murder that have persisted into the 1990s, but no sound, or any vestige of evidence of the ghostly re-enactment is ever uncovered.

I once mentioned the bizarre axe murder on a radio programme and was soon inundated with phone calls, letters and emails from people who had either witnessed the phantom murder at first hand or heard tales about it from other people. One elderly man named George had a fascinating and grisly tale to tell.

In 1968, George was hired to paint the front door and gate of the house on Rathbone Road where the spectral slaughter is said to have taken place. One hot day in June of that year, he was painting the front door when he heard the gate clang behind him. A woman of about seventy years of age wearing a long mackintosh approached the front door. She had a head of curly silver hair and wore distinctive, horn-rimmed spectacles. George assumed the lady was visiting someone in the house, and just stood aside, bidding her, "Good afternoon".

The woman said nothing, but returned his smile and walked into the hallway. George gasped when he noticed that a section from the back of her head was missing. The long gap in the skull was almost elliptically shaped, and the strong reflected light of midday shone right inside, revealing the absence of any brain tissue or any other matter – simply a dark, gaping emptiness. The gap was several inches in diameter, and George knew that no one could possibly walk around in such a state – a wound that size would cause instant death.

On that sweltering June day, George felt goose bumps rise on his skin. He was far too terrified to follow the old lady, but was sure that she had gone upstairs.

When Rita, the middle-aged woman who had hired George came downstairs, the painter told her about the old lady with the appalling hole in her skull, hoping for some possible explanation, although he could think of none. Rita told him that she had heard about the lady in question before, exactly as he had described her, and had dismissed it as a ghostly yarn. But now she turned very pale indeed.

George finished his painting job in record time!

TEMPTING FATE

In Liverpool we have many phrases that mean 'never' – such as 'When the Liver Birds fly away', or 'When Nelson gets his eye back'. Whilst it is very unlikely that the copper-plated birds of flight will ever launch themselves from the domed roofs of the Liver Buildings, and long-dead Nelson will never recover his errant eyeball, there have been incidences where the seemingly impossible has come to pass.

In the 1860s, a pair of lovers in the Calderstones area met whenever they could beneath the ancient boughs of the Allerton Oak, a noble tree that is said to date back over one thousand years. It still stands today in Calderstones, its massive branches supported by iron crutches. Throughout the centuries, it has been a tradition for lovers to make their vows of undying love beneath this Methuselah tree, and in October 1863, a man and a woman kissed beneath its sheltering boughs.

Matilda Walker, a sixteen-year-old maid from a Woolton mansion, and Captain Noel Harrison, a thirty-five-year-old Limerick merchant, took it in turns to make their airy promises.

"I will love you forever," sighed young Matilda. Besotted, she was simply lost in the captain's green eyes.

Captain Harrison was more poetic when his turn came. He held the girl close to his chest and caressed her ear as he made his solemn promise.

"I will love you until this ancient tree falls," he murmured passionately.

Bathed in the light of the moon, the lovers held on to one another. The captain promised that he would marry the maid in the springtime, and he would whisk her far away from the gossiping tongues of Liverpool to live in his old country house.

He told Matilda to meet him at the old tree at a quarter to seven on 15 January – the day he would bring her an engagement ring.

The precious time spent in each other's company soon ended, and Matilda and Noel reluctantly went their separate ways. She watched him leave the moonlit park on his horse before hurrying back to the mansion, where she hoped that her master and mistress would not have missed her.

When Matilda returned she could not contain her excitement. She happily boasted to the other maids about her romantic rendezvous, and the beautiful promise which Captain Harrison had made. Her words fell upon very cynical ears.

"He'll love you until the Allerton Oak falls?" laughed the old cook. "Bah! Typical Irish charmer!"

Matilda found the servants' taunts hard to bear and fiercely defended her lover.

"Captain is an honourable man. Just you wait and see," she said, trying to fight back the tears which were stinging her eyes.

When January arrived at the Woolton mansion with sharp winds and a heavy snowfall, bitter rumours arrived too. It was whispered that Captain Noel Harrison was now courting a distinguished lady in Liverpool and had already proposed to her. Matilda refused to believe the hurtful gossip-mongers, and when 15 January came at last, she managed to slip out from the mansion, swathed in a thick woollen shawl. The time was a quarter to seven in the evening, and Matilda's heart sank when she arrived at the tree to find that her beloved Noel was not there. She pulled the shawl tightly around her and sheltered against the piercing wind in a niche of the Allerton Oak's hollow trunk.

Minutes later, all the negative thoughts about her love for Noel evaporated as she heard a galloping sound. It was Captain Harrison! He hadn't deserted her, but had come, just like he'd promised. He dismounted and tethered his horse close to the immense trunk. The couple embraced and kissed for a while before speaking. Matilda pulled herself away from her love and looked up into the captain's eyes with a sorrowful expression.

"Matilda, my sweet, tell me what is the matter?" Noel inquired.

The maid told him about the cruel hearsay about him being untrue to her. The captain shouted angrily to the snow-laden sky, "Tittle-tattle! Mere tittle-tattle. And you believe these gossipers?"

"No, I don't," said Matilda softly, her concerned eyes betraying her.

"Did my promise mean nothing then?" said Captain Harrison punching the palm of his riding gauntlet.

"Of course!" said Matilda wiping away a tear.

"I told you I would always love you! Until this ancient tree falls!" seethed the captain.

At that moment a great thunderous roar came from afar, and even before it passed through the park, the captain's horse became so terrified it broke loose and ran off, whining in terror. A shockwave shook the snow-covered treetops in rapid succession, one after the other, and the ground quaked. The Allerton Oak rocked back and forth, and Matilda fell backwards into the blanket of snow. Captain Harrison raised his arm and stumbled towards the alcove in the tree's trunk. Two huge branches of the venerable old oak crashed to the ground, narrowly missing Matilda. The apocalyptic tremor and explosive blast faded quickly away, and the silence was suddenly punctuated by the frenzied yapping of hunting dogs somewhere in the distance.

Captain Harrison, his long brown hair dusted with the snow from the fallen branches, ventured out from the alcove and surveyed the damage. He helped Matilda to her feet, and both of them thought about the captain's promise about his love lasting until the famous oak fell, and now it had been rocked to its roots and two of its mighty branches lay in the snow. Perhaps thinking a supernatural force had been at work, the captain suddenly confessed in a roundabout way that he had indeed fallen in love with someone else, upon which Matilda could bear no more. Without a glance back at her love, she rushed back to her workplace, too heartbroken to even shed a tear.

The mysterious force that had damaged the Allerton Oak and persuaded the two-timing captain to confess, originated on a ship on the River Mersey. Just before seven o'clock on 15 January 1864, a ship called the *Lotty Sleigh*, bound for Africa, was just about to put to sea with eleven tons of gunpowder on board, when the ship's steward accidentally spilt some paraffin oil in the hold. A fire broke out and rapidly spread throughout the ship. The cargo of gunpowder ignited and the resulting blast destroyed properties on both sides of the river. The shockwave from the terrific explosion travelled miles across the region, and not only damaged the Allerton Oak, but also felled chimney pots in Huyton, and was heard as far away as Chester. Miraculously, no lives were lost on the *Lotty Sleigh*, and the Allerton Oak still bears acorns today.

THE SIGN OF THE FEATHER

In 1979, a fifty-year-old bachelor named Barry was devastated at the loss of his mother, who was taken by cancer. Barry went to drown his sorrows in The Villiers pub, which once stood at the junction of Elliott and Market Streets, in what is now the Clayton Square shopping centre. Barry's friends at the pub told him he'd get over the loss with time, and consoled him with drinks and their homespun philosophies on life and death. Barry said that he didn't believe there was an afterlife that his mother had progressed to, but one of the drinkers told him that he should open his mind to the possibility of life after death, and perhaps his mother would give him some sign.

Barry was given a lift by one of his friends at the end of the night, and when he walked into the home he had shared with his mum, he was overwhelmed by its silence and emptiness. The drink had fuelled his grief and he was about to wallow in self-pity when he noticed something unusual. On the sofa, he saw a long white feather, resting on a crimson velvet cushion. No one else had the keys to Barry's house, and there was no way a white feather could have blown into the house because the windows were all closed, and, what was more, Barry was observing a long-held local tradition, in which all of the windows were covered with white blinds, to show that someone had died.

On the following day, Barry called into The Villiers and mentioned the white feather to his friends, and they joked that it had probably come from some seagull that had fallen down his chimney, but one of the drinkers mentioned something that Barry had not heard of before. A regular at the pub named Jim claimed that the white feather was universally regarded as a symbol of a deceased person completing their journey to their spiritual destination. Barry found comfort in the thought that it may have been a message from his recently departed mother, her way of assuring him that she had made the journey to the other side and that everything was now okay.

I have received a lot of feedback from readers regarding the white feather phenomenon, and people have put their own different interpretations on to the phenomenon.

One man was looking after his aunt's home for several months whilst she was ill in hospital. Unfortunately, the man's aunt passed away, and on the last visit to her home his curiosity was aroused when he found a white feather, about five inches long, resting on a chaise-longue in the front room. Where it had come from was a mystery, as no one else had access to the house. A relative who heard about the white feather said there was a tradition in the family of such feathers appearing after a death.

In 2002, a woman in Speke emailed me to say that a feather had literally appeared out of thin air before her eyes on a sideboard in her late mother's house, and when she mentioned the feather to a medium, he told her it was the calling card of the angel who had taken her mother to heaven.

MYSTERY MAN

It all began in March 1975 when a Chicago philanthropist, DL Moody, laid the foundation stone of the YMCA building in Liverpool's Mount Pleasant. At the the celebration which took place after the stone-laying ceremony, Mr Moody was handed a letter by a butler. The missive read:

My Dear Mr Moody

Your kind and humane nature is an inspiration to me, sir. I will endeavour to devote my time over the forthcoming months to appoint myself the Robin Hood of the city's slums.
This entails resorting to a life of crime, of course.

Yours faithfully

Mr A Boon

The butler, when questioned about the author of the letter, said that he had simply found it lying on a card table, addressed to Mr Moody.

All of the fifty guests present were shown the controversial letter by the inspector investigating the incident so that he could judge their reactions, but none of the guests would own up to writing it and no one behaved at all suspiciously.

True to his word, the mysterious Mr Boon proceeded to carry out a string of daredevil robberies across the city, and, also true to his word, he posted off hundreds of pounds to scores of poverty-stricken families around the city, using the proceeds of his oddly-motivated crimes. No wealthy Liverpudlians could rest easily in their beds whilst he was still at large.

In April 1875 Mr Boon literally left his calling card at the palatial home of William Graves, a well-known Aigburth millionaire. Some four thousand pounds was stolen together with a large quantity of jewellery. Police raided every pawnshop in the city, but not a single item of the stolen property was ever recovered.

Six police informers were quizzed over the identity of Mr Boon, but apparently no one in the underworld knew anything about him. The robberies, meanwhile, became ever more audacious and prolific.

On one occasion, Mr Boon disguised himself as a widow and covered his face with a black, semi-transparent veil in order to gain entry to a large house being looked after by an elderly butler. Boon trussed up the elderly servant like a Christmas turkey and made off with a fortune and all the family's silverware. A carefully-written note found on the mantelpiece read: 'Pray do not fret, I am merely redistributing your wealth to the needy.'

A week later a wealthy cotton merchant named Angus Critchley – a man who was renowned for being an extraordinary miser – booked into one of the luxurious rooms of the Liverpool Adelphi Hotel. He always carried with him a large wallet, stuffed with cash. He enjoyed the feel of money above everything else and counting it, over and over again, was one of his compulsive pastimes.

Despite secreting the wallet under his pillow before he went to sleep, on the following morning he discovered that it had gone and he was quick to summon the manager and accuse the hotel staff of stealing it. As the manager tried to calm his client down, there came a knock on the door of Critchley's room, where the miser was tearing his hair out at the thought of having had part of his precious hoard stolen. It was the bellboy, carrying a letter for Mr Critchley on a sliver tray. The boy said that he had found the letter on the counter at reception but no one saw it being delivered.

Angus Critchley almost fainted when he read the note, which informed him that he had been 'relieved' of his heavy wallet by a Mr Boon.

The cotton merchant burst into tears at this new affront – he calculated that he had been robbed of almost a thousand pounds, and he vowed that the audacious thief would be brought to justice if it was the last thing he did.

But it was an empty threat, for Mr Boon was never caught.

Only one person ever claimed to have caught sight of the elusive Mr Boon – a nightwatchmen who caught a fleeting glimpse of him at the scene of a burglary in Percy Street, and he described the mystifying thief-cum-benefactor as a sprightly man in his sixties with silvery hair and a kind face.

Beyond that, nothing more is known about Liverpool's own Robin Hood who stole from the rich in order to redistribute their wealth amongst the inhabitants of the slums.

THE BROWNLOW HILL VAMPIRE

I first heard about the basic details of the following creepy story from an article by Richard Whittington-Egan, and it led me on to research the story in much more depth. Whittington-Egan mentioned a bookseller's house on Brownlow Hill which was haunted by an entity, and in researching the background to his story, I discovered that the so-called haunting, believed to have been the work of a poltergeist, had a much more sinister history. This is what I unearthed with my delvings.

In the 1930s, a family at a house on the corner of Brownlow Hill and Trowbridge Street, were troubled by what they assumed to be rats in their cellar. The Williams family heard a loud scratching sound coming from the cellar on many occasions, and so rat catchers were brought in but caught nothing.

One afternoon, there was a loud crash in the cellar, and when Mr Williams went to investigate, he found a huge gaping hole in the cellar wall, and a pile of crumbled old bricks below it. He summoned his brother, and they both peered into the hole with candles. What they saw amazed them. The hole led to what seemed to be a series of catacombs and tunnels. The Williams brothers knew nothing of the so-called Mole of Edge Hill, and naturally wondered who had constructed the tunnels. They heard the sound of someone breathing heavily nearby, and the faint sounds of footsteps. It sounded like someone large and heavy, and the brothers felt very uneasy, so they left the tunnel, and bolted back in to the cellar. During this time, both men could smell something very similar to altar incense wafting from the tunnels.

The brothers ran upstairs and locked the cellar door, and told a policeman, who went to investigate the tunnels later that day with his bull's eye lantern. After a brief exploration of the subterranean passages, the constable returned shortly afterwards, white as a sheet. He told Mr Williams that subsidence was to blame, and that the so-called catacombs were just cellars. He advised him to get the hole bricked up again and left sharpishly. Two relatives were bricklayers, so Mr Williams arranged for them to do the job, but halfway through the bricking up, the men heard strange sounds from the tunnels. They continued bricking up the hole as fast as possible, when suddenly, something very powerful punched through the newly set bricks, scattering them everywhere. The bricklayers fled from that cellar as fast as their legs could carry them, and refused to go back, even to retrieve their work tools.

Mrs Williams refused to stay in the house alone when her husband went to work, because she thought she had seen a very tall man in black dart across the hall one day towards the cellar. Matters took a sensational when an old man in Trowbridge Street claimed that an old vampire was said to have his lair beneath Brownlow Hill. The man was much respected in the neighbourhood and was regarded as a very wise person. He said he remembered people who had gone missing from the Liverpool Workhouse which stood on Brownlow Hill in Victorian times. A 'thing' was said to come from under a slab in the bowels of the workhouse to seize women and children.

Strangely enough, a man who ran Collin's Bookshop on Brownlow Hill confirmed that there had indeed been such a legend. Some said the thing was a ghoul, others claimed it was a vampiric being which lived in a labyrinth of tunnels and chambers under the city. One person in particular was said to know about the strange creature. He was Thomas Whiteside, Catholic Archbishop of Liverpool. He had even sought advice from the Vatican on how to deal with vampires, which are mentioned, or made reference to, in all of the world's cultures. The eating of the body of bread and drinking of wine for blood in the Christian Mass is thought to echo a much older ritual which had vampiric origins. There were stories that Archbishop Whiteside had tried and failed to defeat the thing in the tunnels.

Now we go forward to the mid-1960s. The Metropolitan Cathedral was being built on the site of the workhouse, and the crypt beneath the cathedral was being visited by vandals mostly from Paddington Gardens and the Bullring Tenement. A night watchman named Sugnall was brought in to guard the crypt. In this crypt, which lies deep below the basalt and sandstone of a miniature quarry, there are tombs. There's a vaulted chapel called the Chapel of Relics, and inside there are three large tombs containing the mortal remains of the former Archbishops of Liverpool, Thomas Whiteside, Dr Richard Downey, and Dr George Andrew Beck. These tombs are sealed by a gigantic rolling stone, shaped like a disc. It weighs six tons, and requires machinery to roll it open.

One hot summer evening, the night watchman Sugnall went into the crypt with his Dansette radio and his sandwiches. He sat down in a corner near a small window which hadn't had glass put into it yet, and he was unwrapping his sandwiches – when he felt the ground shaking. The giant disc-shaped stone was moving, turning slowly anti-clockwise, until a black gaping hole appeared. From this gap walked an abnormally tall figure in black, who slipped into the room where Sugnall was on duty.

The figure was insubstantial, like a shadow, or a silhouette, and it was heading straight for the night watchman Sugnall. He couldn't run for the door, because the terrifying figure was in the way, so he turned, and in sheer terror and desperation, he tried to scramble through the small hole where the window pane was yet to be fitted. He smashed his head repeatedly against the small opening in blind panic, and then collapsed from shock and concussion.

When Sugnall woke up the lights were off in the crypt, and he had to feel his way to the door. His hand trembled as he tried each key to unlock the door, and as soon as it was opened, he ran for his life. He was later treated for a fractured skull in the Royal Hospital on Pembroke Place. Sugnall never returned to his old job, and the authorities blamed vandals for the minimal damage to the crypt, which was subsequently re-sealed.

Stranger still, that very same week, there was a series of grave robberies in the cemetery of the Anglican Cathedral. All the robberies took place in supposedly impenetrable tombs. Strange men and women in black had been seen in the cathedral cemetery that week, and police even went to the trouble of visiting schools in Edge Hill and Toxteth to advise children to avoid going near the cathedral on their way home. Considering the vast subterranean legacy of the Mole of Edge Hill, and the other unchartered tunnels of Liverpool, could the Brownlow Hill vampire still be at large beneath the city streets?

THE ANSWER TO EVERYTHING

For thousands of years, people have been looking for answers to the metaphysical questions posed by philosophers and freethinkers. The big questions: Why are we here? Does the Universe have an end and how was it created? Fundamentally, What is the meaning of life? Most people on this planet have turned to religion for answers to these age-old questions, but some occultists and mystics have resorted to the ancient Hebrew science of Gematria – a system by which hidden truths and meanings are discovered within words themselves, by giving each letter of the alphabet a numerical value.

Scientists, on the other hand, have used the seemingly rational science of mathematics to unravel the workings of the Cosmos, and have discovered that number systems, both simple and complex, are to be found everywhere, from within the core of an atom to the complexities of the most distant spiral galaxy.

From these investigations, it would seem that even in the cold realm of mathematics, there is ghostly evidence of some supreme being; some creator at work in this Universe. From the ordered layout of all the known elements and their atomic weights and numbers in the Periodic Table to the double helix of DNA, there is a consistent set of rules and formulae apparent.

Take the curious sequence of numbers discovered by Leonardo Pisano Fibonacci: 1, 1, 2, 3, 5, 8, 13, 21, 34, 55. In this sequence, each number is the sum of the two preceding numbers, and the sequence is found everywhere in nature, from simple things like the positions of branches on a tree and the arrangements of petals on a flower to the layout of spiral galaxies in deep space. Fibonacci numbers are ubiquitous, but no one knows why the mathematical law is so widespread.

Much more astounding than this, was the amazing breakthrough made by Cheshire genius William Jones in 1912. This man had not attended any university and, far from being a professional mathematician, he was a humble working class carpenter from Little Sutton. Yet he could work out the most abstruse calculations in his head, and one day in November 1912, he was jotting down a formula in the margin of a newspaper during a lunch break – the mathematical equivalent of doodling – when he nearly fell off his chair with astonishment.

Jones had assigned a mathematical value to each letter of the alphabet then, just for amusement, he had manipulated a formula to see if it produced words. Whole blocks of text containing actual words in English and other languages were produced by the method, leaving Jones completely dumbfounded. He gradually came to the shocking conclusion that billions of words containing some higher knowledge could be deciphered by using his formula.

This simple, yet ingenious, carpenter wrote to the Royal Society, detailing his discovery, but received no reply. He also wrote to several newspapers, but his discovery never even made it to the letters pages.

Then, one day, in the autumn of 1913, William Jones received a letter from a James Devoy of Liverpool, who claimed to be a professor of advanced mathematics. Devoy said he had heard about Jones' discovery, and was prepared to offer him a huge sum of money if he could see the full formula which had produced the esoteric information. Jones wrote back, accepting the arrangement, and Professor Devoy arranged to meet the carpenter at three o'clock on Sunday 9 November, at Little Sutton railway station.

At the appointed time, William Jones waited on the station platform, naturally expecting Devoy to arrive by train. However, shortly, a 1911 Rolls Royce Silver Ghost came gliding down Station Road and pulled up next to the sandstone building adjoining the station-master's house. The chauffeur left the car and scanned the platform, and Jones tentatively raised his hand, then introduced himself. The chauffeur opened the back door of the Rolls Royce and invited him to step inside. Sitting on the plush leather seats of the car's sumptuous interior, the carpenter met an old man who shook his hand vigorously. The Rolls Royce then silently drove off as William Jones proffered a crumpled piece of paper with his ground-breaking formula scrawled upon it.

Professor Devoy squinted at the symbols and numbers with utter fascination.

"Everything is contained in this one formula," Jones told him, seemingly unaware of how momentous a claim he was making.

"I'm sure it is, sir," said Devoy. "I'm sure it is. I shall be able to extract an astronomical amount of information from the formula using my special calculating and tabulator machines."

Jones couldn't help noticing the excitement in the old man's eyes as he devoured the formula and he warned him to be careful, as the knowledge he had extracted using mental arithmetic was staggering enough.

Jones was paid a mere hundred pounds for his ground-breaking mathematical discovery, and Devoy, having got from him what he wanted, had him dropped off with barely a thankyou by his chauffeur near Eastham Docks. Despite having been given what was to him a large sum of money, Jones felt cheated and angry. He may have been a simple man, but he was no simpleton and he knew the worth of his formula and he also knew that if he had been a recognised mathematician, who moved in the right academic circles, he would have been taken seriously and would have been able to market the formula properly. If the formula's true importance had been recognised he would have become a rich man and would never have had to work again.

Over the next few weeks he soon fell back into the routine of his daily toil at the carpenter's bench, only indulging his passion for mathematics in his spare time. Occasionally he would think of Devoy and the feelings of bitterness would reassert themselves. However, that Christmas, he was intrigued to read in the newspapers of the nervous breakdown of a Professor J Devoy, said to have been brought on by over work. Devoy's condition deteriorated and he never recovered his wits, ending his days locked away in a mental institution. Jones instinctively knew that his mind-boggling, earth-shattering formula had overloaded the professor's mind, with its insights into every aspect of human life.

What was this formula? Well, according to the carpenter, if you calculate the value of Pi – a mathematical value which equals the ratio of the circumference to the diameter of a circle – you get an infinite string of numbers. If you then assign numbers to the letters of the alphabet, you can translate the numbers of Pi into words, and these words, which run into billions, describe everything in the universe.

Just to demonstrate this as a fact, visit this website: http://pi.nersc.gov/ Type in your surname as an example, and the computer will find it encoded somewhere in the billions of digits that make up Pi. The name of your future spouse is there, the date of your death, the name of the Antichrist, along with mountains and mountains of other information. But be careful ... in 1916, William Jones committed suicide. Did the infinite knowledge he acquired through the formula cause him to lose his mind?

DOLLS OF THE DEVIL

We are confronted on all sides by the unknown and unexplained, however confident we may feel in our cocooned, hi-tech world. Our planet hangs suspended in a black sea of infinite space, and not only are we ignorant of what marvels and horrors are to be found hidden in the depths of our Universe, but we know precious little about the elusive realm of what we call the supernatural right here on earth. The following eerie tale is a case in point.

In 1905, there stood a veritable Aladdin's cave of hardware, toys, glassware, kitchen utensils and ornaments at 439 Mill Street in the Dingle. The shop was called Procter's Variety Bazaar, and was one of the most popular stores in south Liverpool, frequented by both adults and children alike.

Days before Halloween in 1905, a man wearing a black, out-of-vogue, three-cornered hat and a calf-length black cape walked up Mill Street, one foggy late-afternoon. He halted at the door to Procter's Variety Bazaar, gazed through the window at the various items on display, then entered the premises. A young shopkeeper, Miss Williams, regarded the unusually dressed stranger with a curious eye, then inquired if she could be of any assistance. Using sign language, the swarthy-featured man conveyed that he was mute, then opened his long double-breasted astrakhan coat and displayed an extraordinary sight to the shopkeeper.

Inside the coat, hanging in a neat row at the inside pocket, was a line of five dolls, each about five inches in height. Three were of men and two of women, all dressed in detailed, realistic-looking attire, including bowler hats and bonnets. The shopkeeper understood that the man wanted to sell the dolls, so she went to consult the store's owner, Mrs Procter. The collection of dolls was purchased for five shillings, and the mute man tilted his hat and left the shop.

As soon as he was out of sight, Mrs Procter displayed the five dolls in the shop window. She was pleased with the unusual purchase, they would fit well with all her other oddly-assorted merchandise, and she announced that she would charge a florin for each one.

On the following morning, a Mrs Briggs stormed into the shop in an hysterical state, and said that one of the five dolls in the window – the one wearing the bowler hat – had obviously been based on her late brother Harold Medlicott. He had hanged himself after being found guilty of fraud at his job in a bank. The doll's face was identical to Harold's and the clothes the figure wore were identical to Mr Medlicott's attire, down to the smallest detail.

"Remove that wicked thing from the window at once!" Mrs Biggs sobbed, "Look at its face! It's our poor Harold to a tee!"

Tutting to herself, Mrs Procter removed the doll in question from the window for a while to appease the disturbed woman, and get her off the premises, but later put it back on display and it was soon sold to a nine-year-old girl named Penny.

Over the next three days, several distressed people came into Procter's shop, claiming that the dolls were the exact replicas of loved ones who had recently died and should be taken out of the window, out of respect for the dead. But Mrs Procter was a keen businesswoman and had paid good money for the dolls. Three more were sold to Penny's mother, but the fourth one was purchased by a man for his four-year-old daughter Georgiana.

A week later, Georgiana's father burst into the shop, holding something wrapped in a tissue. He explained how, two days before, Georgiana had come running to him saying, "Dolly's hurt". The girl had accidentally stepped on the doll, and was alarmed to see real blood and other noxious matter issuing from it. The doll was taken from the child and put on a shelf in her father's study. It soon began to give off a repulsive odour, and seemed to be decomposing.

The slimy object was taken back to the fancy-goods shop where Mrs Procter, by now heartily sick of the dolls and cursing the day she had set eyes on them, was at a loss to explain its deteriorating condition. She could see for herself that something was badly amiss and she reimbursed the man without hesitating.

The four other dolls were also returned in a similar state, and a refund was given for each one. Mrs Procter was furious – the dolls had not only lost her five florins, but had also alienated a good number of her regular customers. She put the horrid, putrefying figurines in a box with a tight-fitting lid and then thoroughly scrubbed her hands to get rid of the smell. Even after several scrubbings with strong carbolic soap her hands were still impregnated with the filthy smell of rotting flesh. She would have thrown the hideous dolls away there and then but she intended giving them back to the man who had sold them to her, along with a piece of her mind and a demand for her money back. However, she didn't get the chance because the swarthy, enigmatic stranger was never seen again.

Weeks later, Mrs Procter was doing a stock take when she came across the box. She gingerly opened the lid, intending to empty it of its weird and repulsive contents, and saw to her horror that it now contained five slimy little skeletons, each dressed in clothes that reeked of decomposition.

Mrs Procter swiftly disposed of the gruesome effigies, and tried to tell herself that the mute man who had created them must have been suffering from some strange mental illness. But for years afterwards a much more chilling thought haunted her mind; had the black-clad doll-maker been the devil himself? Had the dolls indeed been the shrunken forms of real people who had died and lost their souls to Satan because of iniquities committed when they had been alive? The devil is said to have a black sense of humour, and the blood-filled, look-alike dolls of that Edwardian Halloween bear all the hallmarks of his fiendish pranks.

ROCK AROUND THE HAUNTED CLOCK

In 1945, the late comedian Bob Monkhouse was working at Eldon Hall, at Cookham in Berkshire as a cartoon animator. He shared the huge mansion with several other artistic people, and Bob afterwards recalled that late one night, everybody rushed to their beds at one o'clock in the morning, looking as if they were in dread of some impending disaster. Bob was bemused and intrigued by his colleagues' odd behaviour.

Then, at a few minutes to two in the morning the entire household woke to a loud crash followed by a deathly silence so profound that all they could hear was their own heartbeats. Every bedside clock, and several wristwatches, had inexplicably stopped. One of the guests who had been downstairs getting himself a drink had heard the grandfather clock in the hall strike two, and then had watched, awestruck, as the massive timepiece started to rock about violently, and was ultimately pushed over by a powerful unseen force.

The toppled timepiece wasn't badly damaged, and as several guests struggled to right it, all of the clocks in the house started to tick again.

Apparently, that grandfather clock had been bought by a Liverpool man in the 1950s, before being taken to his relative's house in the Crossens area of Southport. Witnesses came forward who said that on certain nights of the year the grandfather clock would chime the hour, then rock back and forth by itself and almost topple over. As the clock swayed, two men in long black hammer tail coats would appear in its vicinity with their hands around one another's throats.

The violent struggle would always conclude with the taller of the two men choking his opponent to death. The strangled man's eyes would bulge horribly and turn blood red from the choking. The figures would then vanish into thin air, and the clock would stop chiming and rocking about and settle back down to its peaceful ticking, the heavy pendulum swinging back and forth as though its rhythm had never been disturbed.

I once happened to mention this strange case on a local radio programme, and received many letters from people in Southport who claimed to have owned the haunted grandfather clock at one time or another. A man from the Churchtown area named Mike said that his aunt had once owned the rocking clock, having obtained it from a Lord Street antique shop.

In 1976, when Mike was fifteen, he and his ten-year-old sister were staying at his aunt's house in Marshside. During the early hours of the morning, his sister sneaked out of bed to get a glass of lemonade from the fridge downstairs, and was stopped in her tracks when she witnessed the materialisation of two men in black beside the grandfather clock as it chimed the hour of two o'clock. The girl let out a bloodcurdling scream that woke the entire household, then ran back to her bedroom in a terrible state. There were several further supernatural incidents concerning the accursed clock, so Mike's aunt eventually got rid of it.

A Southport woman named Gloria also contacted me to say that her mother often talked about a grandfather clock which she had owned in the 1960s and which used to shake and pitch backwards and forwards in the wee small hours. A medium investigated the possessed pendulum clock and urged Gloria's mother to get rid of it as soon as possible. The psychic wouldn't say what she had gleaned of the clock's history, but she had certainly detected an air of evil emanating from it.

The present whereabouts and ownership of the haunted grandfather clock remain unknown.

NAUTICAL HAUNTINGS

THE MYSTERY OF THE GHOST SHIP ALBATROSS

The registers of the world's insurance companies contain many records of ships that have been lost without trace. Modern seagoing vessels, equipped with satellite-based navigational aids, two-way radio and radar, rarely vanish from the sea's crowded shipping lanes, but in times past, many ships sailed into Limbo, leaving not a stick of wreckage to account for their fate. A case in point is the emigrant steamship, the *City of Glasgow*, which set sail from Liverpool to Philadelphia in March 1854, with four hundred and forty-eight souls on board.

There was no hint of impending disaster when the ship steamed serenely out of Liverpool Bay, but she was never to be seen again. Not a shred of wreckage was ever found, and vessels travelling behind the steamship reported no foul or unusual weather conditions which could have accounted for its disappearance. The fate of the emigrant ship still remains a mystery to this day.

As baffling as the vanishing ships are the vessels that are found drifting without crew or passengers. The most famous of these is, of course, the *Mary Celeste*, which was found drifting near the Azores in 1872, in a completely seaworthy state, but without any signs of life on board. The fate of the crew and passengers is the most famous maritime enigma in history and has even become absorbed into the language as a metaphor for a deserted place, but other derelict 'ghost ships' have occasionally been found, not only on the high seas, but also within a stone's throw of our coast. Read further on for my ideas about the fate of the *Mary Celeste*, but for now back to the mysterious *Albatross*.

In the autumn of 1882, George, William and James MacIntyre – three brothers from Southport – were visiting their cousin John Barnett in Lytham St Anne's. They enjoyed several drinks at the local tavern, but were by no means drunk when they left the premises just before midnight. The tavern overlooked the shore at St Anne's, and a thick fog was rolling in from the sea. Mr Barnett heard what sounded like a bell and, because he knew of no buoys in the area, he stopped, and he and his three cousins peered into the depths of the swirling sea mists. The brothers then distinctly heard a second peel, somewhere out in the fog.

Barnett led his cousins down to an old jetty and from that vantage point they could just make out the ghostly outline of a ship that was seemingly resting at anchor. Barnett hailed the ship, but received no reply, and after a while, sensing that something was badly wrong, he convinced the three brothers to row out with him to the apparently abandoned two-masted square-rigger.

Painted darkly across the ship's stern was the name *Albatross*. The ship seemed totally seaworthy from where they sat bobbing about underneath her in the small rowing boat, and Barnett greedily speculated on the substantial fortune to be made if they were to claim the *Albatross* as a salvage prize.

With great difficulty the four men managed to pull up alongside and board the creepy ship. The ship was absolutely silent save for the creaking of her timbers. They found no one on deck and nobody at the helm and the atmosphere on board was decidedly eerie. Keeping close together, they found themselves whispering as they tiptoed around the ship. Then one of the brothers struck a succession of Lucifer matches in order to penetrate the foggy gloom. By feeble match-light, the men explored the captain's cabin, and discovered a skeletal canary lying dead in its cage, apparently from starvation.

In the dank and claustrophobic cabin they could just make out the small blackboard that served as the ship's temporary log. A match was held up to the board to reveal one cryptic word – KILGRIMOL – chalked upon it. Kilgrimol is the name of a legendary kingdom that is said to have vanished below the waves off the coast of Blackpool in ancient times.

Huddling together, the men proceeded down into the cavernous cargo hold. A strange breeze from nowhere blew William MacIntyre's match out three times, so the spooked explorers gave up their quest and clambered back on deck, falling over each other in their rush to get back into the fresh air.

Up on deck once more they sat panting, nervously discussing what to do next. Their instincts told them to get back into the rowing boat as quickly as possible and put as much distance as they could between themselves and the ghastly ship. However, the lure of the salvage money was even stronger than their fear, so, after taking several deep breaths and still full of misgivings, they crept into the mate's cabin.

James MacIntyre was the first to feel his way into the room, his brother William following behind him with the matches. James' foot hit something on the floor, something which rattled ominously. As the match flickered into life, the forms of two skeletons in tattered clothes could be seen lying on the floor. One skeleton was stretched on top of the other, and something glinted in its bony hand. Holding the match closer, the object came into view and the men jumped backwards, falling over each other. A knife! A long knife encrusted with a dark brown material and still firmly grasped in the second skeleton's bony hand and embedded between the ribs of its long dead opponent.

All of a sudden, the dead calm was replaced with mad, raucous laughter which echoed throughout the cabin. Then the ship's bell started to clang unaccountably.

Without further ado, the four men rushed out on to the deck gasping for breath and scrambled madly over the ship's rails to get back to the safety of their rowing boat. They rowed furiously back to the shore, with the ship's bell still clanging in their ears and the unearthly laughter mocking their frantic efforts.

When they reached the jetty each of them was quaking uncontrollably, all attempts at bravado gone. Then the cacophany stopped as abruptly as it had begun. They looked back and saw that the haunted ship had vanished into the night vapours, never to be seen again.

THE MARY CELESTE ENIGMA – SOLVED AT LAST?

One of the greatest mysteries of history is the enigma of the *Mary Celeste*, and that ship has many connections with Liverpool. In 1863, the *Mary Celeste* – then sailing under her original name – *The Amazon* – is said to have collided with a brig in the Straits of Dover, sustaining serious damage. Several crewmen serving on the ship at the time were said to have Liverpool relatives, and there are some who even claim that *The Amazon* came to Liverpool just before the American Civil War. I would not be too surprised if she did, as my city was then one of the greatest ports in the world, and Liverpool's wealth and reputation was largely based on trade with America, particularly the southern states. I have related the folklore, theories and urban legends of the *Mary Celeste* in volume two of *Haunted Liverpool*, but after much research, I believe I may have finally solved this hoary, almost supernatural, maritime puzzle. Here are the facts to begin with.

On 5 November 1872, the two-masted sailing ship *Mary Celeste* left Pier 44 on New York's East River, bound for Genoa, Italy with a cargo of whale oil, fusel-oil (from spirits distilled from potatoes and grain), and one thousand, seven hundred and one barrels of undrinkable denatured alcohol. Because of bad weather, the ship had to drop anchor at Staten Island for two days. An exchange of signals took place between the *Mary Celeste* and another ship three hundred miles southeast of New York, and then the most mysterious vessel in history pointed her bows to the east and headed across the Atlantic.

At the helm of the ninety-six--foot-long ship was New Englander Captain Benjamin Briggs, a thirty-seven-year-old master mariner of enormous maritime experience who came from a seafaring family. The first mate, a veteran of the American Civil War named Albert G Richardson, was a highly competent and trustworthy man. The cook and steward of the *Mary Celeste* was Brooklyn-born Edward Head, and the remainder of the crew consisted of four men, two of whom had a mysterious background. They were two Germans known as the Lorenzen brothers, who claimed to have lost all their belongings on their last voyage when their ship was wrecked. The other two people on the ship who were journeying into the unknown were the captain's wife, Sarah Elizabeth, and her daughter, two-year-old Sophia Matilda.

Eight days after the *Mary Celeste* had set sail for the wine merchants H Mascerenhas & Co of Genoa, the English brig *Dei Gratia* left New York, bound for Gibraltar with a cargo of petroleum. At the wheel was Captain David Reed Morehouse, a man who had dined with Captain Briggs shortly before the *Mary Celeste* set sail.

On the afternoon of 5 December, John Johnson was at the wheel of *Dei Gratia* when he sighted a vessel five miles off the port bow. It turned out to be the *Mary Celeste*, and she was not only sailing erratically, she also appeared to be deserted. The *Dei Gratia* closed in on her, and Captain Morehouse surveyed the ship. He noticed that the rigging was fouled, and parts of it had been blown away. When the *Mary Celeste* was just four hundred yards away, Morehouse shouted to her but no reply came, and he decided to allow his first mate, Oliver Deveau and two crewmen to board the deserted ship. These men soon discovered that there wasn't a soul to be found onboard the *Mary Celeste*. Although the ship was in a far better condition than most seagoing vessels, and there was a six months' supply of food and water on the ship, she had obviously been abandoned in a hurry. The crew had left the *Mary Celeste* so suddenly, they had even left their tobacco, pipes and oilskins behind. The three men from the *Dei Gratia* looked at one another uneasily in the eerie silence.

Superstitious mariners across the globe regarded the eerie incident as some kind of paranormal occurrence. Some believed a giant squid had surfaced from the depths of the Atlantic to pick off the people onboard the *Mary Celeste* with its writhing tentacles, but that outlandish version of events could not explain why the squid would also take the ship's papers, the sextant, chronometer, the bill of lading, the register, and other documents from the captain's cabin. The ship's lifeboat was missing, yet the six months' worth of food and water, plus the crew's tobacco and pipes had been left behind.

The compass had been deliberately destroyed, and the wheel had not been secured with rope – the normal procedure when abandoning a ship. The other mystery concerning the *Mary Celeste* was the unusual route her captain had chosen. Instead of taking the most direct route towards the Straits of Gibraltar, Captain Briggs had steered his ship around the northern coast of Santa Maria in the Azores, coming within a few miles of the islands. Briggs had brought the *Mary Celeste* over sixty miles off course to skim the coastline of a small tropical island. From the information recorded in the ship's log, we know that something significant happened just after eight o'clock on the morning of 25 November 1872, and it took place within the waters of Santa Maria Island.

At the time of the *Mary Celeste* mystery, the Azores had an infamous reputation that stretched back a decade. In 1861, the American Civil War began, and the conflict impacted heavily on Liverpool, because sixty per cent of cotton from the American South came through our city. Under international law, Britain was required to remain neutral, yet Liverpool quickly supported the Confederate states, because the Union was blockading the South's exportation of cotton to Lancashire mills.

In June 1861, a cunning confederate spy from Georgia named James Dunwoody Bulloch arrived in Liverpool, where he made secretive arrangements with local shipyards to build warships for the South. One of these vessels – the *Enrica* – was built by the Laird brothers of Birkenhead, then taken to the Azores, where she was refitted as an armed Confederate cruiser. The Confederate flag was raised, and the *Enrica* was renamed the *Alabama*.

Many of the ship's crew were Liverpool men, and many more Liverpudlians were employed to transfer ordnance to ships on the islands of the Azores, including *Terceira* and *Santa Maria*. When the South lost the war, Confederates such as Bulloch were warned that they would be hanged if they tried to return to the United States, so they remained in exile. Bulloch stayed in Liverpool, and is buried in Toxteth Park Cemetery. Some exiles settled on the islands of the Azores, and from these former Confederate island naval bases, the ex-soldiers resorted to gun-running and piracy to survive. I believe that the *Mary Celeste* became involved in the schemes of these gun-runners.

On 13 December 1872, the *Mary Celeste* was brought to Gibraltar under the remarkable expert hands of a three-man skeleton crew from the British brig *Dei Gratia*. The brig's captain, David Morehouse, claimed the deserted *Mary Celeste* as salvage. There's nothing unusual about a claim for salvaging an abandoned ship on the high seas, but this claim was seen as unique and somewhat sinister, as the *Mary Celeste* was not dismasted or waterlogged – in fact she was completely seaworthy. Mr Solly Flood, the Admiralty Proctor at Gibraltar, virtually accused the crew of the *Dei Gratia* of murdering the *Mary Celeste*'s crew, and he got in touch with Colonel John Austin of the Royal Engineers.

Colonel Austin, incidentally, was a close friend of two people who have surfaced in my research before – General Sir Charles Warren, and my prime Jack the Ripper suspect, Colonel Claude Reignier Conder. Warren and Austin had drawn up the plans for the fortifications of Gibraltar just a few years before. Four captains of the Royal Navy, a Colonel of the Royal Engineers, and the Marshal of the Vice-Admiralty Court suddenly descended on the *Mary Celeste* as she lay berthed in the harbour at Gibraltar. Derelict ships had been brought into Gibraltar before, but none had ever received this much attention. The *Mary Celeste* was inspected inside and out from nose to stern. Surveyors from the Army were called in, and port workers and the curious were kept away from the *Mary Celeste* by soldiers. When a part-owner of the vessel named James Winchester heard about the military involvement surrounding his derelict ship, he immediately sailed from New York to Gibraltar. When he arrived, Winchester saw the ship crawling with the red-coated soldiers of the Royal Engineers. Winchester had a disliking for the English, because many of them had supported the South during the Civil War he had fought in, and he shouted, "By God, I know I have English blood in my veins, but if I knew where it was, I'd cut them open and let it run out!"

With Winchester was his friend Captain Shufeldt, a former Union Navy Commander who had fought for the North in the Civil War. Shufeldt also seemed angered by the British soldiers. As the two Americans looked on, Royal Engineers dived on the *Mary Celeste* to inspect the hull. Colonel Austin, meanwhile, crouched near the huge cast-iron oven hob in the ship's galley. It had been lifted from its four stone blocks and placed a distance away. The hob was so heavy it took four men to shift it. Austin mentioned the out-of-place hob to Solly Flood, and also drew attention to the fact that nine of the *Mary Celeste*'s one thousand, seven hundred and one barrels were inexplicably empty and bone-dry. Had something been removed from those barrels? Had they contained rifles? After the Civil War, American rifles, ammunition and gunpowder had been illegally exported to Europe in the cargo holds of merchant ships. These rifles and bullets had been upsetting the balance of various power struggles in Europe, and the British Intelligence Service knew this, so many ships from America were randomly boarded and inspected by Britain at the gateway to the Mediterranean – Gibraltar.

Under maritime law, a person who salvages an abandoned ship is entitled to a substantial share of the vessel's total worth. Captain Morehouse, his first mate, and two crewmen were given a salvage award of £1,700 for bringing the deserted *Mary Celeste* into Gibraltar. The ship of mystery was kept at Gibraltar for three months as the court of enquiry tried to unravel the fate of her captain and crew. It was said that the *Mary Celeste* had originally been called the *Amazon*, and that she had allegedly visited English ports on many occasions, including Liverpool. The court considered many scenarios in an effort to solve the mystery of the missing crew, but no theory fitted the facts.

Over one hundred and thirty years have passed since the *Mary Celeste* conundrum, and during that time many badly thought-out theories have been churned out again and again. One unrealistic hypothesis was that Captain Briggs heard the barrels of alcohol 'boiling' in the hold and feared that the ship was about to explode, so he and his crew took refuge in a lifeboat that was tethered to the ship by a rope. Denatured alcohol has never been known to have boiled in the cargo hold of a ship on the transatlantic runs, and Briggs was a master mariner of great experience who hailed from a greatly respected sea-going family. He would never have put his wife, child and crew in unnecessary danger by ordering them to leave a seaworthy vessel to crowd into a small lifeboat adrift on the high seas.

The truth behind the *Mary Celeste* enigma lies in another direction. Britain's Intelligence Service suspected many Europe-bound American ships of gun-running. In 1872 there was a Carlist war raging in Spain, and it was fed by many rifles and gunpowder from the United States gun smugglers. There were also rumblings of unrest in other parts of Europe, and gun-runners were doing a roaring trade as a result. The Royal Engineers, stationed at Gibraltar knew this, and they also knew that some of the gun-runners had bases in the Azores, where the Confederate rebels from the American South – and Liverpool – had fitted the *Alabama* warship with guns. The Captain of the *Mary Celeste* had visited an island in the Azores on the morning on which her crew vanished into obscurity.

What was the point of the rendezvous? Nine barrels that never contained alcohol are emptied there, the ships papers are removed, along with the crew, and a huge cast-iron galley stove is removed from its blocks – seemingly because someone had to gain access to something that had been stored under it. A skeleton crew then steers the ship on a course that points it away from the island and they abandon the *Mary Celeste* and return to the island on her lifeboat. The *Mary Celeste* is subsequently scrutinised by four captains of the Royal Navy, a Colonel of the Royal Engineers, and the Marshal of the Vice-Admiralty Court.

In 1884 at a Liverpool society dinner, the Mayor mentioned the strange case of the *Mary Celeste*, which had just been featured in the *Cornhill Magazine*. One man at the table not only had a thorough knowledge of the ship and its crew, he knew the Azores like the back of his hand. The man was Captain James Dunwoody Bulloch, the Georgia-born spy who commissioned the *Alabama* warship to be built at Laird's in Birkenhead. In the Civil War he had taken the *Alabama* to the Azores from Liverpool with a crew that was mostly from Lancashire. People around the dinner table, and Mr Radcliffe, the Mayor, noted that Bulloch had tears welling in his eyes.

"Whatever became of the *Mary Celeste*'s crew?" someone asked.

Bulloch became pale. He shook his head and muttered, "It's all in the past now." Bulloch then left without making an excuse, and without uttering another word. Today, he rests in Liverpool's Toxteth Park Cemetery.

THE SHIP OF THE SEVEN MURDERS

On 9 May 1828, a ship called the *Mary Russell* sailed from Barbados to Cork carrying a cargo of sugar. Her captain, William Stewart, was known as a very kind and gentle man, but for reasons that are still a mystery to this day, in mid-ocean, William Stewart lost his sanity.

His mental deterioration appeared to have started with increasingly frequent and terrible nightmares. He claimed that something evil was hovering over his bunk when he woke up. His devastating nightmares grew progressively worse, and the captain's mental health became increasingly unstable.

On 22 June, Captain Stewart summoned his crew, one by one, into his cabin. Each member of the crew was in turn bludgeoned to death by the crazed skipper. The only survivor was a Liverpool man. Stewart was found guilty of the seven murders but was declared insane and committed to an asylum.

People wondered what had happened to the so-called Ship of the Seven Murders. In actual fact, the ship was renamed *Rose Hart*, but such was her reputation, no one would buy her. She was finally sold at Cork Harbour to a young mariner named Captain John Delaney, who was from Douglas on the Isle of Man.

In July 1832, the newly-named *Rose Hart* sailed from New York to northern Italy with a cargo of petroleum and a crew of eight. One of the crew was a thirty-seven-year-old Liverpool man named Richard Davies. Captain Delaney was reading his bible in his cabin around midnight, halfway through the voyage across the Atlantic, when a Force 8 gale struck the ship, and forks of lightning danced around the dramatic seascape. There were unholy screams from the captain's cabin. When the cook went to investigate what the matter was, he discovered Captain Delaney convulsing and shaking on the floor, foaming at the mouth. What was most disturbing was the fact that his eyes had turned entirely white; his pupils and cornea were no longer visible.

Three more members of the crew entered the cabin to investigate the piercing screams that were echoing along the ship's corridors. The first mate, a Mr Gill, bent over Delaney, when suddenly, the captain leapt upright and punched him directly in the face, shattering his nose. The captain then managed to bolt from his cabin and made his way frantically into the cargo hold. There, he grabbed the ship's axe and tried to smash the hull. He tried to hole the ship whilst simultaneously yelling out dementedly and incoherently.

The ship's cook attempted to wrestle the axe from Delaney. During the struggle, the captain managed to grab hold of some sort of docker's hook and shoved its point under the cook's chin, its sharp tip dimpling his flesh. Suddenly the tip of the hook protruded obscenely from the cook's screaming mouth, like a fish on a line. Delaney seemed to be possessed with double strength. He roared as he lifted the cook high above his head and hitched the hook over a ceiling beam. The cook's shrieks wilted as he passed out in agony, his body limp and hanging grotesquely for all to see.

Another crewman went down into the hold and was horrified to discover the cook's swaying and blood-soaked body dangling before him. Delaney grabbed the axe again and launched it directly into the crewman's back. He died a bloody death in minutes.

Crewman Patrick Kender then tried to attack the rampant captain with a knife. The enraged Delaney swiped again and sliced off Kender's kneecap with the axe, and in an appalling act of sadism, he stabbed his finger through Kender's eyeball as he writhed in agony before him. Before Kender passed out with shock, he managed to ram the knife between Captain Delaney's shoulder blades, but the captain appeared not to feel a thing and remained undeterred, without any sign of weakening. He lunged forward, unstoppable, and attacked Kender's groin. His inhuman attack was extended far beyond obscenity as he chopped and hacked at his victim to perform a brutal castration.

While the captain was engaged in this hideous and savage rampage, his face appeared unfamiliar to those who witnessed it. It seemed to have somehow changed, as if he was possessed. After just thirty minutes, there were only three crew member's left surviving. In sheer, petrified panic they fled on to the deck, closely chased by the demonic Captain Delaney. These poor remaining men were Gill, who attempted to stifle the blood pouring from his broken nose; a young crewman named Williams, who had lost two fingers in the axe assault; and the Liverpool shiphand Richard Davies.

As the thunder rolled and the lightning flashed through the torrential rain, young Williams slipped on the rain-lashed deck, impeding his desperate getaway. Captain Delaney lifted the axe, poised and ready to kill him, but first mate Gill rushed forward and attacked Delaney, punching him twice in the face and somehow managing to dislodge the axe from his menacing and manic grip. Gill was out of breath but mustered enough strength to swing the axe at Delaney, but his grip was not tight enough and it slipped from his hand. The unleashed axe flew through the air and over the rails, flailing into the raging sea. What happened next made young Williams and Mr Davies queasy and faint with fear.

Delaney's frenzied attack had not lessened in its ferocity and he seized Gill's head in a vice-like grip. Violently forcing his hand in to the man's mouth, with a great effort he wrenched Gill's jaw wide apart. The jaw cracked, sinews were uprooted, and Gill's body dropped down hard, twitching spasmodically as his tongue writhed uncontrollably.

Delaney's rage was still not quenched. He moved on to his next casualty and picked up the young cabin boy Williams. Throttling him, he threw the boy's weakly resisting body over the rail into the storm-tossed sea as if he were a rag doll. The mad mariner then closed in on Richard Davies and the Liverpudlian stumbled backwards on to the bowsprit, the long beam at the front of the ship. He crawled along it away from Delaney, who was more manic than before and foaming at the mouth again. The man's hands were heavily bloodstained, and his protruding eyes had heavy, dark circles around them. To Davies, he looked like the devil himself. The captain followed closely and climbed on to the bowsprit. Davies retreated away from this lunging beast until he was clinging on to just the ropes. He could go no further – there was just a watery grave below him now.

"Lord, please deliver me from this devil," Davies howled in desperation.

Almost immediately, before Davies' fearful eyes, the captain's face seemed to alter. His expression dropped and softened and he appeared dazed and confused, as if he had just snapped out of a hypnotic trance. He limply slid back down the bowsprit and landed on the deck, weak beyond exhaustion.

Back on land, Delaney was charged with the murders, and so was Davies, because the court believed that two men must have been jointly responsible. At the subsequent trial, the jury asked: "How on earth could one man wipe out seven men single-handedly?"

In the end Davies was cleared due to a technical point and Delaney was deemed insane and committed to an asylum in London. One night he was heard screaming in his cell, and when the warders looked through the peephole in the door, they discovered that some kind of invisible force was hurling John Delaney up in the air and against the walls. A week later he died in his sleep. During the post mortem, the coroner was puzzled to discover a strange red marking outlined on the dead captain's back which resembled a long claw-like hand.

CURSES

THE CURSE OF THE LONG PURSE

Around noon on the fine sunny Tuesday of 23 June 1891, two loafers sat on the steps leading up to St George's Hall, discussing various hare-brained schemes to make money in an effortless, labour-free way. The two layabouts were thirty-one-year-old John Hagerty of Great Howard Street, and forty-five-year-old Billy Reid of Gerrard Street. Both men were petty criminals, forever on the lookout for that golden opportunity which would mean they would never have to work again. Beneath the grandiose monuments of the history-making men on St George's Plateau, Hagerty and Reid bit their nails and weighed up an assortment of shameless plans to either beg, borrow or steal – anything rather than do an honest day's work.

A tall woman in black approached from the direction of St John's Lane and walked quickly up the steps from the plateau. She wore a black veil over her face, so Hagerty and Reid assumed that she'd been recently widowed. She passed close by them, and as she did so, something dropped from her and tumbled down almost into Billy Reid's lap. Manna from heaven! It was a long, dark-brown, leather purse. A very heavy, jingly leather purse! Hagerty tried to grab it from his friend, but Reid was too fast and swiftly snatched it back. A fight almost ensued.

"Hey! Give it back and share it out, you swine," bawled Hagerty. "It's only routine decency to split it with yer friends."

Reid, still clutching the purse, started to retreat from his colleague.

"Give us half, or I'll go straight to a copper and tell him you lifted a widow's purse," threatened Hagerty, determined not to be done out of his share of the loot.

Because of this threat, Reid ended up giving Hagerty a quarter of the purse's contents, which came to almost five pounds in florins, half-guineas, and sovereigns – a fortune in those days. Inside the purse there was also a small, elegantly-scripted calling card which read: 'Mrs Cluefir, 6 Greek Street'.

The two men immediately set off on a spending spree with their ill-gotten gains, but they soon noticed that the money from Mrs Cluefir's purse seemed to be cursed in some way. Billy Reid bought a bag of boiled sweets for his nephew, and the child choked on the first one he took from the bag.

John Hagerty put two guineas towards the hire of a special wedding carriage for his sister, but after the marriage service at St Jude's, a terrific thunderstorm hit Liverpool and when a lightning bolt struck the church steeple, the horse pulling the carriage fled in terror. The animal careered into a cart and was fatally injured, and the carriage was completely wrecked. The downpour then soaked all of the wedding guests, including the bride and groom. Making the connection between the unfortunate events and the long purse, they threw it into the dustbin, after first removing every last farthing.

But that wasn't the end of their problems – the incidences of bad luck continued, and Billy Reid became convinced that the purse was jinxed, so eventually he decided to retrieve it from the bin and take it back to its owner.

When he called at Number 6 Greek Street, an old woman answered the door, and when she saw the purse, she threw up her hands in horror and told Billy to throw it away at once. The old woman said that people had been bringing the same long leather purse to her house for years after claiming that the money it contained had brought them nothing but death and misfortune.

There was no Mrs Cluefir at the house, and it eventually dawned on the two criminals that the name was a mischievous anagram of the word Lucifer.

"Throw the purse away at once, and go and see a priest," the old woman warned.

Billy Reid did just that. The whole incident acted as a salutory lesson and he decided to turn over a new leaf.

SPRIGGANS

In April 1997, sixty-four-year-old Phil from Knotty Ash was watching television one evening, complaining, as usual, that the soap operas such as *Eastenders* and *Coronation Street* were becoming increasingly boring and untrue to life. His long-suffering wife Lyn had grown immune to her husband's endless and long winded complaints about the quality of television programmes, so much so that she didn't even bother to acknowledge his rants nowadays.

In disgust, Phil turned away from the television and started reading the *Liverpool Echo*, occasionally glancing back towards the television screen, just in case he was missing something. Suddenly his expression changed from one of boredom and frustration to one of sheer bewilderment. The people on the screen had started to move in a sort of slow-motion manner, and the sound had also slowed down to a jumble of deep, unintelligible words.

For an instant, Phil thought it was his cable television box which was on the blink, but when he attempted to turn to speak to his wife, he realised with horror that his entire world had slowed down. One side of his face felt numb, and a peculiarly overwhelming weakness now affected his neck and left arm. Even more alarming was Phil's sudden difficulty in speaking. He could hardly open his mouth, and when he attempted to speak, out came a jumble of slurred sounds which bore no resemblance to what he had intended to say.

Lyn was so engrossed in the soap opera that she hadn't yet noticed that her husband gone limp; in fact he had suffered a stroke. A blood clot in Phil's brain had blocked a blood vessel, killing thousands of brain cells in the process. The cells responsible for speech and bodily movement had been most severely affected but his mind was still functioning normally, although he felt very confused. As he slumped backwards in his chair he recalled his daughter's warnings to have his blood pressure checked, and he also thought briefly about his wife's advice to start exercising instead of smoking in front of the television all day and all night.

He made a concerted effort to call out his wife's name, but all he managed to do was utter a low moaning sound. At last, Lyn turned round, and her eyes widened in shock as her husband toppled forward on to the floor like a rag doll. Phil lay prostrate on the carpet, and although by now he was floating in and out of consciousness, he could hear Lyn becoming hysterical. He was aware of one of his neighbours coming in and grappling with him, and then he heard the same man dialling for an ambulance. Then time came to an end. He did not know whether it was day or night, morning or afternoon, he just caught glimpses of a tiled ceiling and rectangles of neon light in what must have been a hospital.

When he recovered consciousness, Phil began to make a gradual, painstaking recovery as most stroke victims do. He sat in a wheelchair in his bedroom during the long weeks of May, being cared for by his wife, a visiting nurse, his daughter, and sometimes his sister from Fazakerley. Phil could think pretty clearly, but his speech was taking its time to return, and his vision was still a bit out of synch with reality. When they wheeled Phil into the sitting room and placed him facing the television, he would grunt disapprovingly when the soap operas which he despised so much came on.

For some reason, Phil always demanded to be placed at his bedroom window, gazing at the everyday goings on in streets of Knotty Ash. Unbeknown to his family and carers, the effects of the stroke were making Phil see strange things on those streets. Perhaps it would be more precise to say that Phil's stroke had opened up a door into another reality.

One russet evening, just as the sun was setting, Phil noticed a diminutive figure – about two feet in height from his buckled boots to his wide floppy brown hat – come running down the pavement facing his bedroom window. There was something distinctly sinister and malevolent about the figure, the way it waddled as it ran, the way its face was so pallid. Its scrawny little body looked too small to support its oversized head.

At first, Phil doubted his senses, but then he noticed that the neighbours' dog was barking furiously at the troll-like man. The man spat at the animal and the canine reared up with the hair on its back bristling. The dog's owner came running out, but he seemed oblivious to the miniature person. He grabbed the animal's collar and dragged it inside.

Meanwhile, Phil noticed that the little man was lighting up some sort of long clay pipe. He coolly puffed away on the pipe as he stood there, surveying all the gardens and houses of the street. Phil began to shudder as he stared on in disbelief, because he was deeply fearful of the sinister gnome. The bizarre looking character's beady eyes narrowed when they fell upon Phil's house. He stared right up at his half-open bedroom window and seemed to be looking straight through him. Barely able to move, Phil struggled to try and wheel himself away from the window and as he did so he became aware of an overpowering aroma filling the room; it was not an unpleasant aroma, it was similar to lavender. Even in the gathering gloom it was obvious that the smell was drifting up from the pipe which the weird homunculus was smoking.

At that moment the bedroom door burst open and Phil's wife switched on the light as she entered.

"What're you doing sitting here in the dark, love? Come on, let's get you into the sitting room," she said briskly. "It won't do you any good sitting here on your own all the time,"

Lyn closed the window and drew the curtains, leaving only a slight break in them.

"The neighbours will think you're spying on them, sitting here all the time."

As she pulled his wheelchair away from the window, Phil just caught a glimpse of the creature in the street as it darted off into the purple gloom. Phil desperately tried to tell his wife what he had just seen, but all that came out was a series of garbled sounds which, as usual, Lyn misinterpreted.

"It's alright, love. I won't make you watch any soaps if you don't want to, but you know what the doctor said – if you spend hours sitting on your own you'll get depressed. Come on, I'll make you a nice cup of tea."

Phil was determined to make his wife understand him. He became even more animated and motioned to his sketchpad. He attempted to draw the thing he'd seen with Herculean effort, but neither Lyn, nor anyone else, could understand what he was desperately trying to communicate.

All through the following afternoon, Phil watched eagerly from his bedroom window, hoping to see the pipe-smoking dwarf again, but not until after sunset did he notice anything untoward. Down in the street, in the soft amber luminance of the sodium streetlamps, things too fast for the human eye to follow zipped here and there. Then Phil heard faint cackles of laughter and the babble of an unknown language. This time, not one little man, but an entire scrum of them, passed by down the road. The figures were mostly seen in silhouette, but Phil could just make out that they differed in both stature and dress from the original sinister character he had seen.

Phil was fascinated by the odd and strangely enticing beings he was seeing. He kept an eye out for the odd creatures whenever he could, although as he slowly recovered from his stroke, sightings of the leprechaun-like entities gradually dwindled.

One afternoon, as Phil's daughter embraced him, tears flowed from his eyes, and he suddenly said the words, "I love you," very clearly. His speech had finally returned and his recovery went all uphill from that point on. He was eventually able to tell his wife Lyn about the little creatures he'd seen from his bedroom window during his recuperation, and naturally she smiled and dismissed them as hallucinations caused by the stroke. Phil disagreed and insisted he'd seen dogs and cats react to the creatures – he was certain that they could definitely see or at least sense them.

Lyn steadfastly refused to believe in the little men, and jokingly told him that the only little people in Knotty Ash were the Diddy Men, created by comedian Ken Dodd.

Phil felt he was being patronised. Refusing to dismiss what he had seen, he decided to research the folklore and local history of Knotty Ash. Had the Diddy Men been based on some old legend of leprechauns perhaps? After much reading, he discovered that Ken Dodd had based his comical creations on his Great Uncle John Leech, a pint-sized character of bygone Knotty Ash. Phil continued his research and discovered that the old village derived its name from the ancient gnarled ash tree which once stood where the forecourt of the Knotty Ash Hotel is today.

In the eighteenth century, a species of goblin known as the Spriggans made their home in Lancashire. They were spotted in great numbers, congregating beneath the gnarled branches of the Knotty Ash tree in Liverpool. The attire of the Spriggans, Phil read eagerly, included a felt brown hat which matched the description of that seen on the little man.

Two years later, Phil was visiting a spiritualist church with his wife, who had recently lost a close relation. A medium at this church took Phil to one side and informed him that there were little entities accompanying him.

"What do you mean by 'little entities'?" asked Phil, immediately intrigued.

"You saw things you weren't suppose to see a few years ago," said the medium, knowingly. "That's why they're following you."

Phil nodded. Of course he knew exactly what the medium was talking about. The medium earnestly told him that the small, invisible and uninvited guests which were now in attendance would follow Phil till the day he died. He explained that such entities often attach themselves to unsuspecting folk and cause havoc with their lives in the process.

This all struck a chord with Phil. It seemed true enough, as, for the past two years, Phil had been plagued by all kinds of poltergeist activity, and small objects around him had a habit of going missing, never to be found again. When Phil told the medium about this, the psychic man said, "Just be thankful they don't take you. That has been known to happen. People have been whisked away into thin air."

Phil's blood ran cold at this new and even more disturbing piece of information, but he was powerless to do anything to protect himself. He still believes the stroke lifted a veil and allowed him to glimpse the ethereal creatures that most of us are – thankfully – blissfully unaware of.

THE GIRL IN THE RED DRESS

In the severe winter of 1981, a newly ordained priest was at work in his study one night, struggling to write a sermon. Huge snowflakes drifted past the Elizabethan windows, adding a top layer to the heavy snowfall that had already blanketed the streets of Liverpool.

The priest, named Gary, had a number of newspaper clippings of interest on his desk, and had intended to use the topical material they contained for his oration. As he was trying to find ways to incorporate the snippets of information into the sermon, he was interrupted by the bell downstairs ringing three times. Who could be calling at half-past nine on such a bitter winter's evening? Gary wondered, as he fumbled his way downstairs in the dark. The housekeeper usually answered the door at such an hour but this was the one night she had taken off to visit a relative.

Father Gary opened the front door of the priest's house, and saw a little girl, only about eleven or twelve years of age, standing on the doorstep. She had long straight black hair, a pale white face, and a large pair of expressive blue eyes. She wore a beautiful long crimson dress, white socks and black buckled shoes.

In a loud and clear voice, the girl addressed the priest. She urged him to go at once to an address in West Derby, where a Mr Quinn needed to confess something urgently, because his time was near.

"I beg your pardon?" Father Gary said, startled at the girl's unusual request.

West Derby was outside of his parish, and he was concerned about what a girl of her age was doing out alone on such a snowy and bitterly cold night. The girl said nothing more, she simply turned and walked down the steps and turned right, back into the street. The priest walked down the steps after her. He wanted to check that she was safe, but he saw to his utter amazement that she had vanished. He looked down at the fresh layer of virgin snow on the front path, and immediately noticed that she had left no footprints. The priest was more astounded than scared. He walked back up the steps and into the hallway.

Father Gary made his way back up to his study, thinking about the strange experience he had just had. Unable to come up with of any rational explanation, he wondered what the official Church line was on ghosts. He scoured his bookshelves until his eye fell upon *The Catholic Encyclopaedia Dictionary* on the top shelf of the study bookcase. He flipped through the tome until he came to the entry for ghosts. It stated just this:

> GHOST (noun). Catholic ideology has nothing to say against the possibility of a ghost, in the sense of an apparition of one who is dead. It is within the providence of God to permit departed souls to appear on earth to fulfil some good purpose, eg to give help or warning, or to obtain prayers.
>
> The Church also fully recognises the possibility of apparitions or illusions caused by a diabolical agency.

His curiosity aroused, Father Gary decided to do a little research into whether there really was a Mr Quinn living at the address in West Derby given by the strange girl in the crimson dress. He reversed the car from its garage and drove carefully through the snow-carpeted roads and un-gritted black-iced lanes towards West Derby. At every red traffic light, the priest considered turning round and going home to finish his sermon instead of getting involved in what seemed to be a peculiar supernatural matter. Inquisitiveness overrode all such thoughts however, and just under thirty minutes later, he reached the house on Deysbrook Lane, West Derby. It was an expensive looking house, and children had built an impressive snowman in the garden.

The front door of the house opened as Father Gary left the car, and a petite middle-aged woman reached out to lower some empty milk bottles on to the step. She called out in a soft voice: "Modo, come on."

A cat padded softly out of a dark corner of the garden and scuttled into the lit hallway. The woman was about to close the door, when she then noticed the priest standing there. She said nothing, but merely stared as an expression of horror spread across her delicate looking face.

"Good evening. Would a Mr Quinn happen to live here?" Father Gary inquired, feeling awkward and somewhat foolish at the cause of his arrival.

The woman did not reply. She backed into the hallway without taking her eyes off the man before her. Her terror stricken face grew increasingly anxious as she moved backwards into the house and quickly slammed the door behind her.

Father Gary let out a sigh as he turned and went back to his car. He had told himself the notion was ridiculous. He revved his engine for a few seconds as he tried to move away, but his car had some difficulty starting, probably because of the arctic temperatures. When the car finally did start to move, Father Gary noticed a large, thickset man open up the front door again. The man hurried over to the priest's vehicle, and gestured for him to stop. Father Gary wound down his window.

"Did a girl send you here?"

The man's expression was also one of distress and fear.

Father Gary nodded, trying to work out what could possibly be making these two people look so terrified.

The man urged the priest to come into his home, and although reluctant, Father Gary agreed to his wish. Once inside the house, the man poured himself a large vodka with a trembling hand and proceeded to tell the priest a very strange story indeed.

Apparently, a year ago, he and three friends had been drinking heavily in a pub in Wales one evening. With alcohol tainting their judgement, the group foolishly decided to get into their van and set off to the next village to look for some local females. The van had woven unsteadily along a succession of winding and deserted lanes. On reaching a secluded lane, the drunken driver of the van was surprised when one of his friends shouted out for him to swerve. With alcohol-numbed reflexes, the driver was unable to follow the command and kept on moving forwards at considerable speed.

So befuddled was the driver that he remained unaware that he had just hit and killed a young girl. Her red dress had become entangled in the undercarriage of the van and her lifeless body was brutally dragged for a quarter of a mile under the vehicle. The men were genuinely ignorant of the appalling accident, assuming that the van had missed the figure in the road.

When the van was parked and the cold and sober light of day revealed that they had in fact hit the girl, the four men returned to Liverpool. Guilt-ridden, the men feared that their awful secret would surface with dire consequences, although nothing was ever reported. However, soon after, something very strange started to happen. One of the men, named Phil, received a knock on his door just after ten o'clock one night. He opened the door to be met by a priest, who announced that a small girl in a red dress had called at his church and begged him to visit Phil. The girl had claimed with adamance that Phil wanted to confess something before he died. Phil was not ready to confess to anything and insisted that priest leave his premises immediately. Curiously, Phil died in his sleep that very night. His lifeless face revealed a tortured expression that indicated he had suffered some kind of harrowing nightmare just before death.

The other two people who had been in that van on that murderous night both died some months later. They too had received sinister and unexpected visits from different priests, who also claimed to have been sent by a girl in a red dress.

"Are you Mr Quinn?" Father Gary asked with some caution.

The man nodded. He pleaded with the priest for an immediate confession in his kitchen, out of earshot of his wife. The penitent kneeled, and Father Gary listened. After the indepth confession, Mr Quinn shook hands with the priest and Father Gary asked him to come to his church on Sunday. He assured Mr Quinn and his wife that his confession had been heard and that nothing tragic was going to happen.

However, on the following day, Father Gary received a disturbing telephone call. Mrs Quinn's voice was choked as she explained to the priest that her husband had been declared dead on arrival at hospital early that morning. He had suffered a massive heart attack. Mr Quinn was just thirty-eight.

The unaccountable visit by the girl in red that snowy night has haunted Father Gary from that night onwards.

LIBRA

In March 1967 readers of the traditionally staid newspaper *The Times* spotted an intriguing advertisement in the Personal Column, which read:

A witch of full powers is urgently sought to lift a 73-year-old curse and help restore the family fortunes of an afflicted nobleman. Employment genuinely offered.

Many readers of *The Times* no doubt found the advertisement amusing, but the man who placed it in the newspaper was deadly serious in his quest for supernatural salvation. He was the Duke of Leinster, a seventy-four-year-old bankrupt man who had experienced a long run of bad luck in his personal life and financial career.

The ageing aristocrat believed his continual misfortune was the result of an old curse that had allegedly run in the family for seventy-three years. Almost two hundred people responded to the advertisement, and many of them were practising witches, but the particular woman the Duke decided to hire was from Merseyside, and she called herself Libra. She was fifty years of age although she looked twenty years younger.

Just two months after hiring Libra, the Duke experienced an amazing upturn in his luck, and was soon able to pay off all of his debts and re-enter society. Libra remained in contact with the grateful Duke until his death, and in the meantime, the practising wiccan was at large throughout Wirral and the rest of Merseyside and beyond. Libra often gave her services for free, and investigated many hauntings and apparitions.

In 1977, Libra investigated several sightings of a huge phantom black dog with fiery eyes that attacked pedestrians and vehicles on a stretch of Barnston Road, near Heswall. The menacing oversized hound was even encountered by two policemen in their squad car as they travelled down Storeton Lane at one o'clock in the morning. The officers of the law estimated that the dog, which seemed to be of the Labrador breed, had been much larger than a Great Dane, and they too saw the eerie orange glowing eyes of the sinister hound.

The self-styled wiccan Libra encountered and confronted the black dog at a place called Woody Knott at midnight, near to Barnston Road, and allegedly slew the animal with her magic. That night, two witnesses on a farm reported seeing a flash of light at Woody Knott, followed by a red flame leaping fifty feet into the air. Libra said the black dog had been an agent of the Devil, inadvertently conjured up by amateur dabblers in the Black Arts. After that night, the terrifying canine apparition was seen no more.

The most intriguing paranormal incident which Libra dealt with was at Irby Heath in April 1973. Mrs Coombes, a friend of the wiccan, reported the disappearance of her seven-year-old son and four-year-old daughter at nearby Thurstaston Common. Mrs Coombes had been walking with her children when her son had become enthralled by something he had noticed in the distance. He shouted "Wow!" before running off with his sister to the common to take a closer look.

Within seconds they were nowhere to be seen. "It was as if the ground had swallowed them up," a distraught Mrs Coombes told police, unable to explain their disappearance. She also contacted Libra, whose amazing powers were well known. She used a dowsing rod, and told Mrs Coombes that her children were behind an invisible barrier near Thurstaston Common, and that a sinister force was involved. The police heard about this and naturally regarded the wiccan as a crank, but just before dawn on the following morning, Libra arrived at Mrs Coombes's home with the missing children.

The little girl and boy had a very strange tale to tell. They had run to the common after seeing a bizarre-looking man, about seven feet tall, wearing a helmet that was pointed like a dunce's cap, and a close-fitting green one-piece suit. The man beckoned the boy and girl, then pointed to what looked like a giant, indigo-coloured toadstool. The children went inside the 'toadstool' with the strange figure, and discovered it was an ultra-modern house of some sort with futuristic fittings and appliances. The man asked the children if they'd like to live with him and they became nervous and said they wouldn't.

The crazy-looking man had pretended to cry and complained that he felt very alone and needed their company, but the children sensed something sinister was afoot, and hurriedly ran out of the circular dwelling. However, when they ran from the domed house, they didn't get very far, because they found that they were blocked somehow by a type of unseen wall, and they almost knocked themselves out.

The young boy yelped in pain as he clasped his nose, which had almost been broken by this barrier. The helmeted man sounded determined, as he explained that he would be taking them away with him soon, but on seeing the children's reluctance he grew agitated and ended up fleeing into his home – which at that moment vanished into thin air.

It had been at that point that Libra had come upon the scene. The wiccan was obviously alarmed as she ushered the children to safety. She was concerned that the figure was a child abductor from another dimension, and warned Mrs Coombes never to let the children out of her sight again, especially in the vicinity of the common.

One month after this incredible episode, the national press reported that a young boy and girl on the Isle of Wight encountered a mysterious figure fitting the same description as the sinister figure that Mrs Coombes's children had encountered. The article detailed how the children had also been invited into a peculiar dwelling with a strange interior. These children had the courage to accuse the odd man of being some kind of ghost. "Well, not really, but I am in an odd sort of way," he had apparently mused distractedly. When the children asked the man what he meant, he would only say: "You know".

During the thirty minutes in which the children talked to the unusual entity, men working nearby saw nothing, it was as if the children and their other-wordly companion were invisible. Luckily, they were not abducted, and the weird man and his distinctive house vanished.

As for Libra, she passed on in 1998 at the ripe old age of age eighty-one.

MORTALITY BOUQUET

In the following strange tale, I have had to change the name of one of the characters out of respect, but the rest of the story is exactly as you read it. At 69a Renshaw Street there is a wonderful Aladdin's cave of a shop that sells excellent antique, rare out-of-print books, second-hand furniture from various eras, memorabilia, jewellery, clothing, military uniforms, Victorian coins and many other interesting knick-knacks. Several years ago, a thirty-year-old woman named Natasha purchased a small oval painting – which featured a bouquet of red roses – at the Renshaw Street shop. Her boyfriend Dean remarked how vividly realistic the artwork was, and said it almost looked photographic. The oil painting bore a tiny signature that read 'Dominic Love' and on the reverse side of the canvas, Natasha noted that the faded title of the work of art was 'Mortality Bouquet'.

The couple then enjoyed refreshments at the Victorian Tea Rooms at Jeff's of Bold Street, and this was where Natasha took another look at the painting she'd purchased at the Renshaw Street Shop. She immediately noticed that there was something odd about the small painting of the roses, because the flowers had somehow lost their blood-red colouring, and now looked a dull faded pink. Dean also saw that the colour had drained from the petals and remarked that it was very strange.

At the couple's flat in Court Hey, Natasha put the oval painting away in a chest of drawers in her bedroom because she now thought the pink faded roses it depicted seemed uninteresting. The painting lay forgotten in that drawer until one summer afternoon three months later, when a peculiar strong sweet aroma infiltrated the flat. The scent drifted through the bedroom and the hallway, and was hard to trace at first, until Natasha noticed that the smell seemed concentrated near the bedside chest of drawers.

Natasha opened the bottom drawer and the sweet fragrance wafted up to her nostrils. The perfume was apparently coming from the oval picture of the roses – and the petals of the painted flowers were no longer pink, but deep crimson. Natasha took the painting out of the drawer and took a good look at it, just to reassure herself that she was not seeing things. The colour really had somehow returned to the flowers. Dean regarded the painting as sinister, and advised his girlfriend to throw it out, but Natasha was adamant.

"No, I want to see if it changes back to pink again. I wonder if the flowers were painted with some sort of temperature-sensitive paint that changes colour when the weather gets warmer?"

"There's something horrible about it," Dean said enigmatically.

"Ooh, do you think it's evil?" Natasha joked.

Dean was deadly serious, and he opened the windows to get rid of the sickly sweet smell hanging in the air, then went out to buy a newspaper. As Dean was leaving the communal entrance to the flats, he bumped into his aunt – and she was in tears. She had come to break bad news. Her husband Dennis had dropped dead earlier in the morning as he was tending the garden. Dennis had no history of health problems, but the post mortem later ascertained that his heart had been greatly enlarged, and Dennis had died from so-called Sudden Death Syndrome, in which no warning signs or symptoms are evident.

On the day of the funeral, Dean noticed that the roses in the oval painting once again had faded to a drab shade of ash-pink. A week later, the colour returned to the roses gradually over the space of an hour, and during that time, an elderly woman passed away next door to Dean and Natasha.

Dean became convinced that the painting was some kind of harbinger of death; that the inexplicable colour changes it underwent signified the impending death of a relative or friend of the family. Natasha said Dean was superstitious and paranoid, yet over the remainder of the year, the painting was seen to turn blood red on four different occasions, each time preceding news of a death.

Natasha put the painting in the bin in the January of the following year, as she now thought that Dean was right; there was something very sinister about the work of art. A month later, when the disturbing memories of the 'Mortality Bouquet' were fading, a sixty-three-year-old woman named Mrs Dudlowe collapsed outside the flats where Natasha and Dean lived. Natasha helped the lady up and escorted her to the front door of her flat. Mrs Dudlowe's niece answered the door and helped to carry her aunt in to the lounge. Natasha immediately noticed a familiar sweet aroma – and then she saw the oval painting she had dumped in the bin four weeks earlier. Natasha mentioned that she had once possessed such a painting and Mrs Dudlowe's niece blushed.

Natasha later heard from neighbours that this niece often went rooting around in people's bins in the area on the orders of Mrs Dudlowe, because the nosy old woman liked to read the discarded documents of her neighbours. Telephone bills, supermarket receipts, letters from the DSS, final demands to pay a bill, and so on. The niece of the pathologically prying Mrs Dudlowe had probably found the accursed painting in Natasha's wheelie bin during one of her night-time delves into the refuse.

An ambulance turned up at the flats and despite receiving cardio-pulmonary resuscitation at her home, Mrs Dudlowe was dead by the time she was taken into the local hospital.

The whereabouts of the unlucky painting are unknown, and I can find no information on Dominic Love, the artist behind the malign work of art. So the mystery surrounding the sinister painting remains unsolved. I would be interested to hear whether any readers have heard of the accursed painting.

VISIONS

THE FAMILY OF THE CHURCHYARD

In June 1860, a dilapidated old cottage, built way back in the days of King George III, stood on the rural outskirts of the Islington area of Liverpool. Its thatched roof was leaking and mildewed, and most of the filthy window panes were either absent or cracked. Yet within its damp walls, a small family had huddled together for several months, scratching together an existence.

Not one member of this family was related to the other by blood, yet it was undoubtedly a family anyway, with strong ties, having a father and mother at its head, with three daughters and five sons. The father was sixty-six-year-old Dr Jonathan MacDougall, a snowy-haired physician who had lost his career to alcoholism after the death of his wife three years before. The mother of the family was a widow, fifty-three-year-old Mrs Henrietta Hayden, who carried with her a heavy burden of grief, having made a spiralling descent into the slums after surviving a fire that killed her husband and children. She was prone to frequent and prolonged fits of crying.

The youngest of the five sons was Bobbo, a skeletal infant, abandoned on a doorstep by his thirteen-year-old mother, and rescued from death by exposure by Mrs Hayden. Then there was six-year-old Georgie, who had once worked in a weaving factory, scrambling under machinery, risking life and limb, to retrieve cotton bobbins during his eighteen-hour working day. Now his industry-induced lung condition was too serious for him to be employable any longer. Georgie's hopeless ambition was to one day ride a horse, and Dr MacDougall had promised his ailing adopted son that he would ride the finest Andalusian horse when their situation had improved.

However, their present situation was going from bad to much much worse now that a ruthless landlord and his men had turned up at the cottage, broken down the door and evicted everyone without a thought for their welfare. The sick and bedraggled discards stumbled in bewilderment away from the landlord and his lackeys in the relentless pouring rain, homeless yet again. They all blindly and trustingly followed Dr MacDougall. Too weak to protest, the only sound was the wheezing and coughing of little Georgie.

The wrecks of humanity were only a stone's throw from the large elegant houses of the rich, but no one of any class ever acknowledged them in their miserable wanderings.

Amazingly, this story was to have a happy ending. By an extraordinary twist of fortune, the 'family' of Dr MacDougall were camped out in St John's churchyard one chilly September evening, when salvation finally arrived from an unexpected quarter. Little Georgie was groaning in Mrs Hayden's arms, coughing pitifully, and MacDougall sat next to them on a bench, quite sure he was about to die from hypothermia as an invading icy chill crept up his numb legs. Dr MacDougall had never been a religious man, but as he bowed his head and the damp and cold engulfed his whole body and froze his brain, he struggled to pray to whatever God might be out there, asking him earnestly for help; any little sort of help at all.

As he prayed, the bitter, tissue-destroying cold induced strange imaginings and visions which did not seem to be simply dreams. In one such vision, out of a golden sparkling light, a bearded man dressed in a long tunic reminiscent of some biblical prophet came forward and announced, "Help is on its way".

The doctor's eyelids flew open and he sat up with a jolt. At that moment, a passing stranger, swathed in scarves, stopped in his tracks before him.

"Doctor MacDougall?" he asked hesitantly, addressing the head of the family, in an astonished tone.

The stranger was none other than James Nugent, only son of Sir Bernard Nugent, one of the wealthiest men in the country.

Many years ago Dr MacDougall had been the Nugents' family doctor and had once successfully treated young James when he contracted scarlatina. When James Nugent discovered how the old family doctor was living, he invited him to his mansion in Aigburth. Dr MacDougall said that he could only accept the generous offer if his adopted family could accompany him. James Nugent was a generous man and said they'd be more than welcome, and not only did he take them all off the streets, he later gave Dr MacDougall a large, twelve-roomed house on Duke Street to accommodate his motley family members.

From that day onwards, MacDougall's family decided that they should all share a common name and they chose the apt surname of St John, after the churchyard where they had all once slept, and where they were resumed by the kindness of James Nugent. The St John family attended church regularly and became a respectable, prosperous family. Dr St John set up a successful medical practice, and shortly before his death, at the age of seventy-three, he took thirteen-year-old Georgie St John on a trip to Spain, and enjoyed watching him fulfil his dream of riding a fine white Andalusian horse.

THE SANDMAN

Many years ago a Birkdale man named Mr Drake told me that on some summer evenings in the 1960s, he often saw a shadowy figure on the sands of Southport. The ethereal entity used to appear as though it was sinking into quicksand only to resurface from another part of the beach. Mr Drake was not the only person to witness this bizarre sight.

Mr Drake's father claimed that the apparition was of the so-called 'Sandman', an old mariner who committed suicide (for reasons unknown) by walking out to sea in a drunken state in the 1860s. The following tale is derived from an article in the *Daily Mail* in 1922, and it concerns a mysterious entity that is alleged to haunt the beaches of Southport. Perhaps the ghost is that of the mysterious Sandman.

In June 1918, three American soldiers stationed at Southport decided to take advantage of the sea, sand and sun, and went down to the beach to relax. The armistice was just five months off, but the British Empire had lost over a million lives in the great conflict. America had entered the war eight months previously in November 1917, and there had been a great influx of US troops in to the ports of Liverpool and Southport.

The three American privates camped out on Southport beach were all aged eighteen. They were Tom Bradley of Duluth, Minnesota, Jim Daniel of Logan County, West Virginia, and Solomon Harris of Fargo, North Dakota. In three days the young men and the rest of their regiment were set to travel down to the south coast to be shipped over to France, but until then, the teenagers intended to grab plenty of fresh air at the beach, and while doing so, planned to eye the English roses promenading with their boyfriends, and hopefully even see some of the local girls bathing!

The three young men sat in deckchairs, much further out on the beach than the locals. An elderly woman strolling along the beach with her small dog stopped and advised the soldiers to move further inland because of the infamous fast incoming tides, but the three men didn't take her advice. Happily ignorant of the consequences, the Americans talked enthusiastically about boxing, the opposite sex, their sweethearts and families back home, and their ambitions.

"When the war's over I am going to buy me a yacht so I can sail the Great Lakes," said Tom Bradley, relaxing into his deck chair. With boots off and his broad rimmed hat tilted down to shade his red baby face, it was as if he had no worries in the world.

'Solly' Harris chipped in that he hoped to run a farm after the war and raise a big family. He painted the picture well, describing how he would build the biggest still and sell his grandma's moonshine by the barrel-load. The introverted, soft-spoken Jim Daniel admitted to his two friends that he planned to go prospecting for gold before retreating and building himself a shack in the Appalachian mountains.

One hour later, the soldiers returned to their barracks, but when they were once again given a short recreational period of leave in the evening, the three young men made their way back to the beach after taking in the twinkling sights of the Lord Street. This time they walked further out, almost to the water's edge, making uneasy jokes about their mortality and what fates they could meet in France.

At that moment the skies suddenly darkened. Each young man felt a knife-edged coldness permeate his uniform, and gales gusted in from the Irish Sea, howling like Celtic banshees. The soldiers quickly and unanimously decided they'd had enough of the changeable British weather and turned briskly around to go back to their base. It was in that instance that they heard a voice. It drifted towards them from very far away in the distance. Someone was crying out for help, but the cries were indistinct because of the advancing roar of the rushing tide.

"Someone's hollerin' out there," said Solly Harris, staring to the north west with his hand clamped down on his hat. There was an uncertain quiver to his voice that his companions detected.

The teenagers waited, squinting against the sharp wind, trying to see where the frantic voice was coming from.

"It's a gull, Solly," Jim Daniel decided, but his friend told him to be quiet. They listened for some moments longer. The wind dropped for a few seconds, and all three soldiers heard the voice of a man shouting out for help.

"Over there," Tom Bradley pointed westward to a faint black spot in the distance.

Three pairs of young eyes could just about discern a man who appeared to be engulfed and up to his shoulders in sand. He was sinking, and the foam of the rolling tide was almost upon him. The three Americans did not hesitate and raced out to the trapped man's aid, but they found the quicksand around him so treacherous, they were forced to exercise the utmost caution in their rescue attempt, lest they lose their own lives as well. They could just make out that the man wore a leather jerkin and a white shirt with puffed pagoda sleeves. His hair was long and curly, quite unlike the usual short and neat hairstyles of the time. He not only looked old fashioned, but spoke with a decidedly vintage English accent.

"In the name of charity sir, help me," he pleaded.

Tom Bradley took action. He lay himself down flat on the wet sand and tried to crawl out to the man, but could only look on with his comrades in horror as the man was suddenly pulled under by the suction of the quicksand. The man's hand slid under the sand, a momentary and sinister final salute as the incoming tide swilled up around the space which was now bare. Realising the danger they were in, the soldiers had to make a run for it. Their feet clung heavily to the damp sand, but they managed to wrench themselves away towards safety.

The three young men reported the tragic incident to the local police. From the description of the quicksand victim given by the soldiers, the police assumed the dead man had been a vagrant.

Two days later, the three soldiers returned to the beach for their final visit before their departure. They felt uneasy as they recalled the awful occurrence on those very sands just days before. The time was almost 7pm. Each young man knew that in the morning they would board the train that would take them to Kent. From there they would be ferried to France, to fight at the front.

As the trio trudged along there was silence. Each young man's deep and foreboding thoughts were eased by the repetitive swirling sound of the tide as it lapped in. Their thoughts were disturbed by a familiar voice crying out in the distance. Once again the skies darkened as a turbulent storm suddenly blew inland from the sea.

The soldiers were astonished to see that there before them once more was the odd-looking man, sinking, just as before, in the sands, close to the predatory water's edge. Curiosity drew them near enough to the man to see that he wore the same leather jerkin and white shirt. They tried to make sense of the fact that there, just feet away from them, was the same long haired man who had perished two evenings ago before their very eyes. The soldiers instinctively backed away this time, as it quickly dawned on each of them that the figure sinking once again below the sands must be a phantasm. When they looked back towards the spot from the safety of Marine Drive, they each saw the silhouette of the man partially emerge from the sand for a while, before steadily sinking back until he could no longer be seen.

Two of the American troops were killed in action in France. Tom Bradley survived, and later recalled the strange tale of Southport's haunted beach to his family and fiancée back home.

OMENS IN THE SKY

Strange things have been seen in the skies over the North West over the years, and I am not just referring to UFOs. In the first volume of *Haunted Liverpool* I mentioned the 'city in the sky' seen over Liverpool in September 1846. My main source for this extraordinary spectacle was a detailed report in the *Transactions of the British Association for the Advancement of Science* of 1847. A Dr DP Thomson reported in that staid publication that:

> On Sept. 27, 1846, about 3 P.M., an erect image of Edinburgh, depicted on the clouds over Liverpool, was seen by two residents in the Great Park at Birkenhead, for a period of forty minutes.

Other people, on both sides of the River Mersey, saw the gigantic object in the clouds. Onlookers found the vision to be reminiscent of the magical floating island of Laputa from Jonathan Swift's classic, *Gulliver's Travels*. To modern minds, the flying city could be interpreted as a huge spaceship that was perhaps carrying out a survey of nineteenth century England. We will probably never know the truth.

Across the Irish Sea, the 'Duna Feadhreagh,' or fairy castles, have long been reported on the coasts of Antrim, Donegal, and Waterford, and one wonders if these fairy castles were mirages or actual visions of something real.

Omens of death and disaster have also been seen in the world's skies. In May 1876, for example, General George Custer and the six hundred men of his Seventh Cavalry Regiment rode off from Fort Abraham in Lincoln, Montana, to join up with other soldiers who were ready to attack the Sioux Indians. As the Seventh Cavalry Regiment rode off, people waving them goodbye were alarmed to witness what they could only describe as an astonishing mirage. Half the troops riding off appeared to actually rise up and drift away into the sky before suddenly vanishing. This was interpreted as a terrible omen, and people wondered if it was meant to imply that half of Custer's men would meet their deaths in the wars against the Indians. In the following month, the Battle of Little Bighorn took place, and Custer and two hundred and sixty-four of his soldiers (close to almost half of his regiment) were killed by the united tribes of the Sioux Indian nation.

Of course, nearer to home, stranger things have been seen in the sky. On Saturday 2 September, 1905 people across North Wales and North West England witnessed a bizarre-looking creature flying at an altitude of two miles. To most people the unidentifiable object moving around in the sky was a dark spot, but to those who examined it with powerful telescopes and field glasses, it was seen to be a terrifying creature. The Cambrian Natural Observer and Astronomical Society of Wales documented the bizarre description of this creature, which was taken from the comments and notes of many amateur and professional astronomers throughout the North West region of England and Northern Wales.

'It seemed to have four legs and looked like a Sphinx with wings and webbed feet,' claims one astronomer. Others said the 'monster' looked demonic with black skin and must have been enormous to be visible at a height of two miles. At a Welsh schoolhouse at Vroncysylite, some people who scrutinised the flying object with telescopes shuddered, and many of the religious people in the area believed a demon from hell was flying over Wales, and they all breathed a sigh of relief when the black winged creature was lost from sight and the blue sky. Five days after the unusual visitation a purple-red substance fell from the sky, at Llanelly in Wales. To this day, we are as ignorant as our Edwardian forebears in fathoming the origins of the inscrutable flying creature.

In May 2004 I received a significant number of emails from people in Liverpool who allegedly beheld the impressive vision of a gigantic black horse galloping across the sky during a sunset. A woman in Norris Green was in her back garden when she saw the spectacular horse, galloping in almost hypnotic slow motion across the low banks of a cumulus cloud. Seconds later the horse was nowhere to be seen. Just what the meaning of such a gigantic black horse is, remains anybody's guess.

MYSTERIES EXPLAINED

MADAME LALAURIE

Marie McCarthy arrived at Liverpool in the summer of 1839 on a merchant ship called the *St Lawrence*, which had sailed from New York. Among the crew of that ship was a certain eighteen-year-old cabin boy named Herman Melville. The teenager was destined to become one of the greatest writers of all time one day, but Marie McCarthy was destined for a grisly date with her conscience.

Beneath her hood, Marie's long dark hair was tied up in a knot, high upon her head, with well sculpted curls and loops above the ears. Through the rain of an out-of-season downpour, her beautiful but cold blue eyes surveyed the dock, and the stevedores, and the crowds of people at the quayside, surging forward to greet family, friends and loved ones newly arrived from New York. She had no loved one waiting for her in this foreign land, only a business acquaintance of her late husband's; a man named Troy Ellis, and she was to meet him in the Liver Hotel at Waterloo.

Later that day, a carriage took Marie to the hotel, and there she met Mr Ellis. He, like Marie, was from Louisiana, and spoke with a southern drawl that the young Creole lady found comforting being so far from her home. Miss McCarthy rested for three days at the Liver Hotel, while Mr Ellis made arrangements to provide her with the type of luxurious accommodation she had been accustomed to at New Orleans, before she was forced to take flight.

A house on Abercromby Square near to St Catherine's Church was bought outright. Miss McCarthy had more than enough money to buy fifty such houses, although no one was certain of the source of such flowing finance. She rarely attended balls and soirées, but when she did

Marie McCarthy gave away little information on her past and the origin of her wealth. Gold diggers tried to woo her and bank managers tried to advise the lady, but it was always in vain. Mr Ellis played a protective role and would try to intervene and fend them off.

Strange rumours began to circulate about the house on Abercromby Square concerning dreadful female screams heard in the dead of night. Some thought the wealthy young American was demented with having so much money, yet no love in her life.

In 1841, a twenty-year-old footman named William Priest was employed at the house of mystery, and the tall athletic youth soon became romantically involved with Miss McCarthy, despite the efforts of Mr Ellis to thwart what he considered to be an unsuitable romance. William and Marie went on a romantic sojourn to Paris, but whilst in the French capital, Marie encountered two gentlemen who called her 'Madame LaLaurie', and spat at her and accused her of being evil. Miss McCarthy and her lover were forced to flee in a carriage to avoid a scene, and Marie assured William that it had all been a case of mistaken identity.

Back in Liverpool, strange things began to happen at the house on Abercromby Square. The sounds of chains being rattled were heard to come up the stairs at midnight, and in the early hours of the morning, the sound of women and children's wails could be heard. One evening at eleven o'clock, William Priest was lying besides Marie McCarthy in her four poster bed, when they heard the distressing sounds of the rattling chains nearby. On this occasion, a procession of silhouettes crossed the wall at the end of the room. The shadows of men, women and children with chains leading from one neck to the other, walked in a single file across the lavishly decorated walls. Upon seeing this uncanny spectacle, Marie let out a scream and hid beneath the covers.

The hauntings seemed to follow Marie, whether she was in her bedroom or at a hotel, and by the Christmas of 1841, she suffered a mental breakdown. When William Priest called at the house on New Year's Eve, he was told that Marie had taken her own life by cutting her wrists, three days before. Troy Ellis showed him the blood-soaked bed, and the open coffin. William wept over the coffin, then left the house for good, unaware of the true identity of the woman he loved.

For many years in Liverpool, nobody knew the dark history of Marie McCarthy, and in 1841, the inquisitive people of Liverpool's élite society would have paid dearly to learn what I am about to relate to you.

Marie McCarthy was, in fact, Delphine McCarty LaLaurie, a wealthy socialite from New Orleans. In 1831, she and her husband, the eminent physician, Louis LaLaurie, purchased a beautiful majestic-looking mansion at 1140 Royal Street. Madame LaLaurie revelled in throwing lavish soirées in which she entertained the most prominent people in New Orleans with no expense spared. Madame LaLaurie was not only renowned for her spectacular parties though; she was perhaps better known for her immense retinue of well-behaved slaves. At this time, there were rumours about Delphine's cruelty towards her slaves, but no one could have guessed the full shocking extent of her barbarity.

Delphine was a woman of striking, angelic beauty, and when she travelled through New Orleans in her sleek phaeton coach, driven by a regally dressed slave, she was quite a sight to behold. On many occasions, Madame LaLaurie would throw a handful of pennies on to the cobblestones for the children. To the young ladies of New Orleans, Delphine McCarty LaLaurie was a role model, but behind the splendour and respectability, there lurked a monster of a woman.

In the kitchens of the LaLaurie mansion, Delphine kept the black cook chained within twenty feet of the fireplace, where her indulgent and sumptuous meals were prepared. No visitors were ever aware of this shocking state of affairs, because people from outside the mansion were never allowed into the kitchens.

One afternoon in 1833, a neighbour of the LaLauries heard a child's scream at their courtyard. The neighbour peeped out through the lace curtains and saw a little black slave girl of about eight years of age, running across the courtyard of the LaLaurie mansion, and in hot pursuit was Delphine LaLaurie, brandishing a bullwhip and screaming at the child in French. The slave girl, Leah, had been combing her mistress's long tresses, and had caught a knot in Delphine's hair, which was pulled by the comb. In a fit of rage, Madame LaLaurie had seized a bullwhip and chased the petrified little girl out of her boudoir.

The neighbour watched in horror as Delphine chased the girl up four storeys and on to a balcony that ran over the carriageway. As Madame LaLaurie ascended the stairs with the whip, Leah tried to climb over the rail of the balcony, but lost her footing and plunged back down to the courtyard. Her limp and broken body lay there, totally lifeless, as Madame LaLaurie's cousin arrived just metres away in his carriage. He was astonished to witness the tragedy. The neighbour continued to observe the dreadful proceedings, and she watched Delphine LaLaurie pick up Leah's tiny body and take it into the house. The same neighbour also observed shadowy figures burying the slave girl's body in the corner of the courtyard after dark.

The authorities investigated the concerned neighbour's allegations, and in the end Madame LaLaurie was merely fined three hundred dollars for not declaring the death.

At that time in New Orleans, there was a slave-protection law in force which ordained that slaves who were subjected to cruelty would be automatically taken from their owner and sold at public auction. However, slaves that were taken from Madame LaLaurie and sold at auction often ended up as her property again, because the sadistic socialite would arrange for her rich relatives to buy the slaves at the auctions and then give them back to her.

The misery and cruelty which the slaves endured at the hands of the deceptively angel-faced woman continued for some time, until April 1834, when the cook announced to the other slaves that it would be better to die than to live such a wretched life at the LaLaurie mansion, and she set the house on fire. The fire brought the immediate attention of both the local populace and the fire brigade. When the firemen turned up at the mansion, they were directed by the slaves to a small attic crawlspace that was bolted and locked from the outside. Whimpers and moans were heard from inside this confined, claustrophobic room, and a battering ram was used to gain access. The firemen had been exposed to death and disfigurement many times before, yet even the seasoned fire officers were not prepared for the hideous sights which awaited them within the tiny room.

Inside the small room were at least a dozen slaves, chained to the walls. They were maimed and disfigured, their bones protruding through their skin from chronic malnutrition. It was subsequently discovered that many of these poor souls had been the subject of crude medical experiments. One man had been turned into a eunuch by barbaric surgery. The most horrifying sight was that of a woman locked inside a cage small enough to accommodate only a small dog. Her arms had been amputated at the hand of Madame LaLaurie and her skin appeared to have been peeled off in sections. Another victim of the inhumane Delphine LaLaurie had all of her arms and legs broken and the joints reset at odd angles so that she could only move along on her stomach in a hideous crablike manner.

One wild-eyed woman, once freed from her shackles, ran in terror past the firemen and jumped through a window immediately to her death. Two of the slaves had died from smoke inhalation, but the ones that survived were given sympathetic pensions. The slaves revealed how Madame LaLaurie whipped them mercilessly each morning after breakfast to satisfy her sadistic cravings. As firemen sifted through the fire-damaged mansion, they came across a variety of body parts from the mutilated slaves, stored in jars and upon shelves.

As the disgusting news about Madame LaLaurie's treatment of her slaves spread, the enraged townspeople demanded rough justice and sought her out, but Delphine and Louis LaLaurie, and their loyal coachman, had already fled from New Orleans. The LaLauries abandoned the coachman once they were safe, and he made the mistake of returning to New Orleans, where the mob stabbed the horses and destroyed the carriage. The coachman was battered to within an inch of his life, but was lucky enough to live through the ordeal. The appalled crowds then returned to the LaLaurie mansion and burnt what remained of the former grand residence to the ground.

It was said that Louis LaLaurie died in mysterious circumstances not long afterwards, but no trace of Madame LaLaurie could be found, although there were many rumours about her whereabouts. Some said she had gone into hiding in France, whereas others claimed that the evil woman had been seen at New York, waiting for a passage to England.

In fact, Madame LaLaurie had boarded the *St Lawrence* at New York under the assumed name of Marie McCarthy, and with a trunk full of diamonds, gold and jewellery, she had headed for a port in England that had always had amicable connections with the American South – Liverpool. It seems though, that the vengeful spectres of her victims had also travelled with the wicked, butchering murderess, and had haunted her conscience until she was forced to take her own life.

Some say that the body of Delphine LaLaurie was shipped back to New Orleans to be buried by relatives at a secret location. We may never know where her body lies, but I think we can safely assume where her soul is.

THE BLOOD THIEF

I came across the following strange story whilst performing research for my book *Wicked Liverpool*, which is about various murders and crimes on Merseyside. One snowy night in the winter of 1899, a thirty-year-old Liverpool bookseller named William Jaggard of 139 Canning Street was having difficulty sleeping. He got out of bed, poured himself a glass of scotch, and sat in the dark, gazing out the window at the silently falling flakes of snow. The street below was deserted. Suddenly, a type of four-wheel horse-drawn cab, known as a growler, came around a corner and stopped outside Number 83.

William Jaggard opened his window out of curiosity and looked down the snow-covered street. Just visible beyond the glare of a lamp-post a strange scene was being enacted. Two men in top hats flecked with snow were dragging a young woman into the house. As Mr Jaggard leaned out of the window, he was able to see that the men were pushing the girl up the steps and into the house. The carriage moved off without a sound into the night.

The next morning at seven o'clock, William Jaggard called at the house into which the woman had been taken, apparently against her will. It was the house of Arthur J Elwyn, a prominent surgeon. A maid answered the door, and when Jaggard told her he would like to see the surgeon, the maid said the master of the house could only see him by appointment, as he was a very busy man. Jaggard mentioned the incident he had witnessed, and the maid went to tell Mr Elwyn. Minutes later, the large thick-set surgeon appeared at the door, irritation etched on his face.

"What is all this nonsense about a young woman?" he asked sternly.

William Jaggard told him what he had seen and the surgeon told him he must have been mistaken, and he slammed the door in his face.

Jaggard walked away, and as he did so he saw a policeman – a PC John Mann – coming down the street on his beat. The bookseller walked along with the policeman and told him about the men dragging the woman indoors at Number 83. PC John Mann was responsive.

"Just between you and me sir, I've heard of a lot of strange comings and goings at that house, at all hours in the morning," he confirmed.

PC Mann was on the Bedford Street beat on the following night, and this was where events took a sinister turn. Part of John Mann's beat was Abercromby Square, and as the policeman patrolled the street, he stopped under the shade of a tree and enjoyed a cigarette for a few minutes. As he did so, he saw a carriage trundle into the square and come to a halt outside one of the fine Georgian buildings. The door of one of these grand-looking houses opened, and out came a tall stout man in a top hat with side-whiskers. He had hold of a young lady by her arms, as if he was restraining her.

The driver of the cab came down and opened the door, and they put the woman in the vehicle. The man in the top hat climbed in with her. PC Mann prided himself on his perfect 20/20 vision, and he could see that the man wearing the topper was none other than Arthur J Elwyn, the Canning Street surgeon. The carriage moved away and headed out of the square.

PC Mann finished his cigarette and continued on his beat, down Chatham Street, across Falkner Street, into Sandon Street, then right into Canning Street. When PC Mann was proceeding along Canning Street, he met the bookseller William Jaggard. Jaggard ran up to him excitedly.

"The surgeon Elwyn and a man dragged a woman into his home. There were fits of screaming!"

PC Mann walked along the street, and he saw another constable in the distance, standing on the corner of Catherine Street. The other constable had a beat that interlocked with his patrol. PC Mann flashed his bull's eye lantern at the policeman, and his colleague immediately came to his aid. The two policemen went to Number 83 and PC Mann pounded on the door. There was no answer, but the policeman continued to knock.

"Police! Open up!" he called out.

He heard a bolt was being drawn, and a maid answered in her nightcap.

"What is the meaning of this?" she grumbled, clearly not appreciating the interruption.

At that precise moment, a woman's dull scream was heard in the house, so the policemen – and William Jaggard – ran into the house. They listened to the screams, and traced them to a backroom upstairs. When they burst in, they saw Arthur J Elwyn and an assistant, Mr Hinchingbrooke. Three women were in the room. One woman, who was aged about eighteen, was bound up on a table and gagged. A tube led from her arm into a large bottle – full of blood. The men saw that there were pints of blood in bottles all around the room. The other woman, who was of similar age, was screaming and clawing the surgeon's face as she struggled to get off the table. The third woman on the table beside her, was about thirty, and appeared rather distinguished. There were tubes connected to her arm too.

There was a scuffle as the policemen and Mr Jaggard apprehended the surgeon and his assistant. Amidst the brawl, a large glass vessel containing blood was knocked over and smashed. Red globules of blood seeped across the slate floor. The surgeon's feet slipped and slithered as they became coated in the spilt blood as he wrestled with PC Mann.

The surgeon and his friend were arrested but no charges were ever made, and the reasons for this remain unknown. It transpired that Arthur J Elwyn had been attempting to transfuse blood into an unidentified well-to-do woman, who had lost a lot of blood after giving birth through what is known as a postpartum haemorrhage. She was desperately ill.

Mr Elwyn had been carrying out dangerous and illegal experiments in blood transfusion, and was attempting to take the blood from unwilling donors who had been coaxed into entering his home with promises of money. Arthur Elwyn had studied the work of the British obstetrician James Blundell, who had performed the first successful blood transfusion in this country in 1818. Blood groups weren't discovered until 1901 by Karl Landsteiner, so at that time Elwyn had been taking a great risk with his extreme experiments.

BUNNEY'S BABY SNATCH

Once upon a time, when Britain had a global empire, and Liverpool was the second city of that empire, the great ships which lined up on the Mersey carried cargoes of exotic goods from every corner of the world. A sizeable percentage of the foreign merchandise ended up in Bunney's department store, one of the greatest emporia which Liverpool has ever had. Situated at the junction of Church Street, Lord Street and Paradise Street, it was the place to visit if you were after unusual novelties, curious and oriental goods.

One mellow Saturday afternoon in October 1904, thirty-year-old widow, Margaret Wheeler, was abstractedly browsing through the extensive range of chinaware on the second floor of Bunney's. Her blank expression betrayed the fact that her mind was not on the beautiful array of porcelain displayed before her. She was thinking instead about the days when her dear late husband Charles used to come to the store with her. He had died from influenza two long years before, and now Margaret felt hopeless, lonely and depressed; she felt that her life was over. Love would never come again, and she felt too old to try and find another husband. In any case, who could ever possibly replace her beloved Charles?

Margaret Wheeler was infertile, or 'barren' as it was known in those days, according to her doctors, and she wondered, as she had often done before, if the pain of the bereavement would have been easier to bear if she had only had a child by Charles, a living reminder of her dead husband. The child-that-never-was haunted her dreams and invaded the thoughts of Margaret's waking life, and she felt the loss of this imagined child almost as keenly as she felt the loss of her dead husband.

Suddenly, on that fateful afternoon in Bunney's, Margaret was faced with an unbearably tempting opportunity to cure this terrible empty ache. An adorable little girl, aged about two or three, with curly golden hair and a cherubic face, was standing before her, obviously lost, sucking her thumb and with tears welling up in her big blue eyes. Meanwhile, her young, shabbily-dressed mother was rushing away from her down the stairs, and she was crying too.

In the space of a heartbeat, Margaret scooped up the abandoned girl and hurried down the aisle to another staircase. She walked out of the store in a daze, wondering if it was all another cruel dream. Along street after street, she rocked the sobbing child in her arms, convinced that everyone around knew that she was a child abductor. The child was heavy and struggled in her arms. She carried her as far as she could and then, to placate her, she took her into the cocoa rooms on Brownlow Hill, where she was treated to a cake and a glass of milk and gradually stopped crying. A waitress smiled at the child and asked Margaret what her name was. She was stuck for words for a moment, then quickly decided on Bunney, from the store where she'd found the little girl. The waitress leaned over the child and gently spoke her name, but there was no reaction.

Margaret paid for the tea and cakes, and twenty minutes later, still clutching the little girl, who by now was behaving much calmer, caught a tram home to Shaw Street. Obviously the neighbours would soon notice the sudden appearance of an unfamiliar child, so Margaret hastily packed her bags and went to stay with her old aunt Vera in Southport, who would hopefully understand the abduction.

Vera was deeply shocked when her niece told her how she had come by the child, but Margaret threatened that she would commit suicide if Rose, the name she had since decided to give the child, was given back. Vera spent many hours trying to reason with Margaret. What about the child's mother? What about the police? Surely there would be a nationwide hunt. However, although she scanned all the newspapers daily and listened avidly to the television news, there was no mention of any missing child and she had to acquiesce in the end and allow Margaret to keep the child, against her better judgement, and despite deep misgivings.

Margaret, meanwhile, seemed oblivious to the implications of what she had done, and was busy planning out her new life as a mother. She had it all worked out; she and Rose would move into an isolated seaside house with no neighbours, and her little girl would be educated at the best public school. In a few days' time she would take the child on an outing to London to buy her some toys and new clothes; she was determined that she would have the best of everything.

Unbelievably, she seemed to have got away with the abduction, that is until two months later, when the real mother of 'Rose' – sixteen-year-old Mary Regan – had a sudden crisis of conscience, and went to Prescot Street police station, confessing how she had abandoned Mary junior in Bunney's department store. A full investigation was launched, and statements from the waitress at the Brownlow Hill cocoa rooms and a former school friend of Margaret Wheeler's who had bumped into her with the child near Moorfields, ultimately led the police to the missing child.

The bewildered tot was wrenched screaming from Margaret's arms and returned to her mother. Margaret was never charged with abduction because the authorities were sympathetic to her distressed state of mind following her bereavement. Sadly, poor little Rose no longer got the best of everything when she was returned to her mother and she died from a fever two years later in the slums of Everton.

For Margaret Wheeler, however, things turned out more happily. A year later, the doctor treating her for depression ended up proposing marriage, and several years after the wedding, at the age of thirty-three, despite being labelled as barren, Margaret bore him a child.

She named the child Rose.

EVE'S APPLE

On the beautiful sunny Saturday afternoon of 13 May 1876, crowds from across the north west of England converged on Anfield Cricket Ground, which is now the site of Liverpool Football Club's stadium. The legendary WG Grace, the British Empire's most celebrated cricketer, was batting for Dingle against the Anfield team, and amongst the multitudes surrounding the pitch, there sat two high-class gentlemen – William Rowlands and Alexander White – reclining languorously in their deck chairs as they sipped champagne and smoked their Havannas.

Anyone viewing the pair might well have assumed that the topic of their conversation was the cricket game at hand. However, it was neither the cricket, nor anything as mundane as the weather, or the current economic situation which was being discussed. No, Rowland and White were discussing the possibility of killing a trouble-making woman. Elizabeth Cochrane, a widow of Napier Terrace, Canning Street, who had discovered that her youngest maid, seventeen-year-old Jemima Jones was six months pregnant to the same Mr William Rowlands of Duke Street, a forty-five-year-old moneyed loafer.

Six months before, in December, the beautiful but naive Jemima had been walking along to her mother's old house in Everton one snowy Saturday afternoon, when she had foolishly accepted the seemingly kind invitation of a lift in Mr Rowland's carriage. Young Jemima soon succumbed to the wily charms of the older man-about-town, unaware, of course, that he was married to a wealthy, but plain-faced heiress, and that his intentions towards her were anything but honourable. Jemima was taken, not to her mother's, but to Rowland's luxuriously furnished pied-à-terre; a secret house which he kept on Seymour Street, where William Rowlands regularly chose to spend some decadent time away from his frumpish, unsuspecting wife.

Once inside his clandestine hideaway, William took the blushing Jemima by the hand and led her to a sumptuously decorated bedroom. There, upon the satin eiderdown of a large, four poster bed, he laid out several gorgeous dresses for her to choose from. When he returned to the room, the innocent young servant, who couldn't believe her good fortune, was standing, transformed, before a long mahogany mirror wearing a beautiful pink evening dress and a gleeful smile from ear to ear. William flattered and fussed over Jemima until she was convinced that she was the most beautiful creature in the whole city.

The rogue then escorted her to a prestigious restaurant in the centre of Liverpool where he wined and dined her and afterwards they went on to a spectacular Christmas musical at the Empire theatre. Finally, when they arrived back at Seymour Street, she was treated to even more champagne. The poor child lapped up the attention along with the champagne, which went straight to her silly, pretty, little head which, being totally unaccustomed to alcohol, was soon swimming in a most alarming fashion.

Taking advantage of Jemima's inebriated state which had caused her to drop her customary guard and forget all her mother's dire warnings about the scurrilous intentions of certain so-called gentlemen, the cad then made love to her.

On the following morning he paid a hansom cab to drop her off at her employer's house at Napier Terrace. Mrs Cochrane read the unmistakable signs of infatuation in the dreamy expression on the maid's face, and told her that her brother in Everton had paid a visit to the house the previous evening, anxiously enquiring about Jemima's whereabouts. Young Jemima was an honest girl, and she blushingly poured out to Mrs Cochrane everything that had happened. Her employer was outraged that she should have been taken advantage of in such a way. She demanded to know the name of the scoundrel who had done this to her.

"All I know is that his name is Jim," murmured Jemima, her head bent in shame and tears welling in her eyes. "He really was a fine gentleman, Miss. I'm sure he meant no harm."

"Fine gentleman, indeed!" scoffed Mrs Cochrane. "What sort of a fine gentleman would treat a young girl so? Where does this scoundrel live?"

"Erm, on Seymour Street, Miss. A beautiful house, full of fine furniture and ..."

"That's enough, child ..." said Mrs Cochrane, quietly.

As soon as she heard about the house on Seymour Street, she paused for a while, and seemed to soften. Her eyes became misty, as if some long buried painful memory was being dredged up.

Trying to keep her emotions in check, Mrs Cochrane then asked if this Jim had a small mole, just above the right edge of his upper lip. Jemima confirmed that he had, and, between sobs, asked her employer if she knew who he was.

"Mmm. I wonder ..." Mrs Cochrane mused to herself, ignoring the question.

Jemima then confided in her that Jim had arranged to pick her up again on Thursday evening outside the Philharmonic Hall.

"He wants to see me again, Miss," she said. "So perhaps his intentions are honourable after all."

Mrs Cochrane said nothing and, when Thursday came, she did not stop Jemima from going to meet her lover. Instead, she followed her, at a distance, to the rendezvous spot. She was dressed in black, with a long shawl and a black velvet bonnet on her head so as to make herself inconspicuous. She stood on Hope Street, in the shadows outside the illuminated area of a lamppost. There, seated in the hansom cab, her suspicions were confirmed – the cad who was consorting with Jemima was, without a doubt, William Rowlands – the very same despicable bounder who had deserted her twenty years ago for Eve Wickenden, a wealthy heiress.

Jemima was about to climb into the cab when Mrs Cochrane hurried over and stopped her. When Rowlands saw Mrs Cochrane he didn't recognise her at first, but after hearing her distinctive voice, he soon realised who she was.

"You're a married man, Mr Rowlands," she said, "and, what is more, you are old enough to be this girl's father!"

Not a word of reply was given, and without so much as a glance in Jemima's direction, William Rowlands slammed the door of the hansom, and slid back the small door in the roof of the vehicle to give instructions to the driver. The hansom cab trundled away across the cobbles, towards the northern end of Hope Street.

That same evening, Elizabeth Cochrane sat at her bureau and penned an anonymous letter to Eve Rowland, informing her of her husband's extramarital affairs. Eve Rowlands was a quiet woman who never showed her emotions. She read the anonymous letter without a flicker; it merely confirmed the gossip she had overheard from the hushed conversations of the servants. For quite some time she had suspected her husband of infidelity – for one thing he spent such long periods of time away from the house and refused to tell her where he was going, or how long he would be gone.

Usually long-suffering, the letter seemed to trigger something inside Eve and she decided to resort to a very dark revenge upon her wayward husband. She sat before the apple tree he prized so much in the back garden of the Duke Street mansion, and smiled as she refined the details of her plan of retribution.

The months passed, and when, in the following year, Jemima Jones discovered that she was pregnant with the child of William Rowlands, Mrs Cochrane and her teenaged maid visited the home of Eve Rowlands. Eve told Elizabeth that she would soon be divorcing William, but hinted that she also had some kind of punishment in mind, and seemed purposely vague about the course of action she was intending to take.

As all three women were gathered in the drawing room, William Rowlands entered, and became speechless for a while when he saw Jemima, his wife, and an old flame sitting together. Looking him straight in the eye, Eve told him that she intended to initiate proceedings for divorce on the grounds of adultery, and that her solicitor brother would make sure that every penny of her inherited fortune remained securely in her bank account. William Rowlands denied the affair at first, but soon realised that this was one situation which he would not be able to wriggle out of so easily. So, being the master of resourcefulness, he adopted a different tactic, and fell to his knees and begged Eve to give him a second chance.

"I was a fool to stray!" he sobbed, his head in Eve's lap. "No man could ask for a more beautiful or loving wife."

Eve's resolve and plans for retribution seemed to have evaporated; she said that she loved her errant husband and had therefore decided to give him one final chance. Elizabeth Cochrane warned her that he would never change and anyway, what was to be done with poor Jemima who was bearing the fruit of his treachery. William Rowlands felt that, for the time being, these three women were holding all the cards and Jemima Jones was paid a huge sum of money as compensation, and remained at the house of her employee.

However, the whole affair left William Rowlands seething with resentment and so, on a Saturday in May 1876 at Anfield Cricket Ground, we find him plotting various ways to kill Mrs Cochrane – the woman who had exposed him as an adulterous womaniser. He offered his friend Alexander White a thousand pounds to shoot Mrs Cochrane, but Mr White declined.

"What would be achieved, William?" was his answer. "It could have the direst consequences."

William Rowlands proposed various ways of disposing of Mrs Cochrane but each proposal was met with objections from his more cautious friend.

In the event, William's villainous plans were superseded by those of his quiet but cunning wife. Far from having forgiven him, she was busy scheming her revenge.

In the autumn of that year, William Rowlands contracted a mysterious illness whose symptoms were acute nausea and stiffness of the limbs. The doctor diagnosed acute dyspepsia – inflammation of the stomach due to eating too much rich food – upon which William called the medical man an ass and said that he had never over-indulged in food in his life. Indeed, for the duration of his illness William ate nothing except an apple a day from his favourite tree in the backyard and quantities of nourishing broth, all washed down with mineral water. Yet it soon became evident to his doctors that he was being slowly poisoned by minute degrees.

A fortnight after first contracting the illness, William crawled from his sickbed, writhing in agony from the inferno of pain in his stomach, and he died as he attempted to crawl down the stairs. The coroner recorded death from an unidentified irritant poison as the cause of William Rowlands' swift demise, yet a detective had found no trace of poisons in the home of the dead man. The broth was checked, and so was the mineral water, but nothing suspicious was detected.

Many years later, Eve Rowlands finally revealed how her husband had been poisoned. In May of 1876, Eve's solicitor brother, Howard, had bought, at her bequest, a pound of potassium cyanide from an electroplating factory on the dock road, and had carefully buried the highly toxic lump of poison among the roots of William's prized apple tree. By the autumn, when the apples had ripened, they contained barely detectable, but nevertheless, lethal, amounts of poison that had been drawn up from the roots. It had all been highly experimental, and Eve was not sure if her scheme would work, but the results far exceeded her expectations, and to her mind at least, brought about a rapid and well deserved end to her husband's infidelities.

Afterwards, the tree was chopped down, and had to be carefully disposed of, because if the wood was burnt, it would give off highly poisonous fumes.

RAT'S CASTLE

In the 1840s, two petty criminals, named Jake Tipping and Toby Campbell, went on the prowl in Liverpool one evening, looking for places to burgle. Being well known in the south of the city, the crooks paid a visit to the neighbourhoods of the north. They kept watch on a strange looking and secluded house that was situated near a large stone quarry off Prescott Lane (now called Prescot Street). An old grey-haired man hobbled out of the place that evening, and within earshot of Jake and Toby who were hiding near the quarry, the man said hello to some gentlemen who were walking down from Low Hill. The men greeted the oldster as a "Mr Harrison" and the two burglars heard the elderly man say he was going to spend the weekend with a relative in Islington. The men told Mr Harrison to be careful walking alone to Islington, as two shady characters had been seen in the area. The men kindly volunteered to accompany Mr Harrison to his sister's home, and as the old man and his escorts walked off, Jake and Toby peered at them over a slab of quarry sandstone.

The criminals moved stealthily towards the crooked-looking house, and within minutes, Toby Campbell had picked the rather old-fashioned lock on the front door. In the stone-floored hallway the crooks froze. An enormous bull stood there, stock still, perhaps about to charge, but curiously, it never moved. They soon realised it was stuffed! It was actually a particular bull which had bolted from a farm and fallen to its death in the nearby quarry many years before.

The thieves searched the intriguing house and found a small bag containing a few gold and silver coins in one room. As they rummaged through drawers and cabinets in the kitchen, the aroma of freshly baked loaves hung heavily in the air. Jake Tipping, the greedier half of the burgling duo, also saw a large pan of ragout on the hob, and even the cold mouthful of stew he sampled tasted delicious. Toby laughed at his audacity.

"Yous have always been a greedy 'un, Jake. Eatin' on the job now! Better mind that old codger doesn't come back and find us in here."

Despite this caution, a few moments later Toby was blithely putting woodchips in the hob and soon managed to get a roaring fire going. It wasn't long before the two rogues were enjoying bowls of steaming hot stew. Toby had even found three green bottles of unlabelled wine in the cellar, and they emptied the bottles into flagons and supped heartily.

"Tastes vinegary, don't it?" remarked Jake, as he stifled a belch. He exhaled deeply and wiped his sleeve across his swinish face.

Toby gulped down the drink and glanced at the huge oil painting of a black rat, hanging with some superiority, over the fireplace. He was puzzled as he stared at it. The rat was an unusual subject for a picture. His gaze then fell upon an odd-looking pipe on the stone mantelpiece. Next to the long, spiralling pipe, there was a pouch containing black tobacco. Clearly not content with the liberties he had taken so far, the lawbreaker pinched clumps of it with his fingers and stuffed it in the pipe bowl. He lit the pipe and sucked on it, but the taste was too strong for his liking, and he coughed loudly.

"Quiet Toby! You'll have the law on us!" Jake said, in between more mouthfuls of his second gluttonous helping of stew.

Toby tutted in response and inspected the pipe. He looked more closely at the tobacco and saw that the black fibres were, in fact, insect legs. He recoiled in horror, and threw them to the ground. The pipe fell, sending incandescent orange sparks into the hearth.

"Toby! You clumsy fool! What's wrong with you?" Jake hissed, with the soup ladle poised before his dripping mouth.

Toby was spitting with repulsion as he told Jake about the insect legs. His complaints were dismissed as nonsense, as Jake lit a candle and went to root around in the kitchen.

"The more I eat, the more I want!" he smirked.

He opened a cupboard, and by the light of the candle, he saw rows of jars. He leant in to inspect them and saw that they contained pickled mice, worms in oil, slugs in water, cockroaches in butter …

Backing away from the cupboard in shock, Toby almost set fire to Jake's hair with the candle. As Jake also studied the provisions in the cupboard, the burglars looked at one another in disgust – and wondered what had been in the stew. The texture of the succulent meat and spices they had just heartily eaten suddenly turned very sour on their palates.

The two thieves left the house with a certain urgency. They were attacked by waves of nausea, and headed straight to an old tavern nearby which stood on the site now occupied by the Coach and Horses at Low Hill.

Some of the stolen money was used by Jake and Toby to buy large measures of Scotch and gin. They felt so sick and dizzy just thinking about the jars of pickled insects and rodents. The crooks hadn't been at the tavern for more than an hour when a night watchman visited the inn and told the landlord that Mr Harrison's home had been broken into. A local man in the area had seen two figures leaving the house and had alerted the police.

"Why would they break into Rat's Castle?" the landlord queried, as he served a customer. "They must be mad!"

A while later, Jake and Toby could not resist asking the landlord what on earth this Rat's Castle was.

With macabre delight, the landlord explained that the peculiar building situated near to the quarry down the road was nicknamed Rat's Castle because the eccentric old Mr Harrison who lived there ate 'rat meat' and prepared revolting dishes using ingredients such as cockroaches, snails, spiders and other vile constituents. Harrison even made his own distinctive wine, 'fortified' with rat's blood. The reclusive old man claimed that he owed his longevity and good health to his novel eating habits – particularly his stews, which were made from flies, cat's brains, earth-worms, potatoes, moss, carrot fungus and blood strained from moles.

Jake and Toby hurried out of the tavern and immediately both men vomited violently right there in the street. So affected were they by the vile concoctions they had feasted on, that they were bed-ridden for days. On their next meeting, both men vowed that in future they would never eat at the house they had broken into!

JESUS AT LIME STREET

In the eyes of twelve-year-old Tommy O'Rourke, Jesus had arrived at Lime Street Station in a cloud of steam, with thunder rolling ominously in the heavens over Liverpool. This was on the Saturday morning of 7 July 1957, as rain hammered down on the great arched metal and glass roof of Lime Street Station. A man with dirty-blond shoulder length hair, with a Sacred Heart beard and moustache, emerged from the cloud of locomotive steam and smoke, carrying only a battered suitcase. He didn't wear a halo like the Messiah depicted in the oval pictures at his school, St Malachy's, yet Tommy still sensed that the man was very distinctive.

The biblical-looking man wore a modern dark blue suit. He strode down the platform, attracting sarcastic glances and bemused looks from the other train travellers as he passed them – long hair for men was frowned upon in the fifties. Tommy, however, didn't laugh at the stranger's appearance, he was transfixed by him.

"Excuse me, sir," said Tommy, catching him up.

The man halted, turned, then stared down at the boy with a pair of sad, brown and infinitely expressive eyes.

"Are you ...?" Tom's courage suddenly faded and he wasn't sure if he was asking a silly question. His voice trailed off.

After a pause, the tall man answered him in a well-spoken voice, "Who do you say I am?"

The boy's face flushed deeply and he looked down in embarrassment at the man's sandals.

"Out of the mouths of babes comes the truth. They will not accept me, but the eyes of a child behold me," said the man with a smile.

"Are you ... are you ... Jesus?" Tommy managed to stammer out the burning question.

"Thine own lips have said it," said the man with a gentle smile, just as two colourful Teddy boys, running to catch a train, brushed past him, swearing and laughing at his appearance.

"Get yer 'air cut mate!" one of them bellowed.

"Judge not according to appearances!" shouted the bearded man, his voice resounding with some authority. He held the eye of the Teddy boy who had made the remark.

The Teddy boy responded to the challenging voice and stared back at the long haired gentleman, while quickly reaching into his pocket, perhaps to get his flick knife, but his friend dragged him away and on to the stationary train waiting at the platform.

Tommy was fascinated by the man who stood before him and the odd scenario he now found himself in. One minute he had been running to escape the rain by sheltering at the train station, wondering what to do with himself, the next minute here he was face to face with Jesus of Nazareth. He smirked to himself at the thought of the fantastic essay he could write about his school holidays when term started again at school.

Tommy decided to join the intriguing man as he walked away from the station and along Lime Street. The two figures walked on, shrouded by the mist of rain still falling, until they reached the Continental Café. In the man walked, with Tommy tagging close behind. He proceeded to order breakfast, and treated Tommy to an ice cream. When asked by a canny-looking Liverpool waitress whether he wanted extra toast, the man simply waved her away, quietly saying, "Man doth not live by bread alone."

The biblical quotation went straight over the waitress's head, and she chewed her gum and squinted at the man in puzzlement before wandering off to talk to a regular at another table.

A flutter of concern entered Tommy's thoughts. He knew his parents had warned him not to trust strangers, yet he felt incredibly safe with the man, almost instinctively, and had a sneaking suspicion the figure before him really was Jesus.

The rain eventually gave way to pleasant sunshine and a stunning rainbow formed high in the sky, as Tommy and the man walked out of the café. As he had no fixed abode, the man made some enquiries about obtaining free shelter. Tommy stood behind the figure, simultaneously in awe and in fear, as his eyes fell upon the gathering of down-and-outs. He closely followed the man as he made his way over to the vagrants who were gathered outside on Lime Street, and politely asked their advice on where he could stay for the night. Most of the vagabonds replied with hostility, swearing at him and mocking his old fashioned appearance. There was just one tramp of a gentler nature named Anthony, who offered some help, because, he claimed through a drunken slur, that the modern-day Jesus had apparently driven devils out of his hysterical meths-drinking wife in the Legs of Man. Anthony politely, if a little hazily, directed the man he perceived to be an exorcist to the Vagrant's Hostel on Shaw Street.

After walking along a little further together towards the hostel, the man turned to Tommy.

"We must part here," he told Tommy, "for this is not the place for an innocent child. Go home, young man, and tell all you meet on the road that the Kingdom of God is at hand."

"Will you be alright with them?" Tommy eyed the assortment of rough-looking hobos sitting on the steps leading to a once fine Georgian House.

The man nodded, and placed his hand on Tommy's curly head. "The innocent pure-hearted child is nearer to Heaven than the most devout Archbishop," he said softly, before entering the hostel.

Tommy felt a strange sadness at their parting, but wandered off towards his home in the Dingle. On his way he passed his school, St

Malachy's, and bumped into the school's priest, Father Keeley.

"Father!" Tommy shouted. The stout rosey-cheeked priest turned to smile, then continued on his way. Tommy chased after him. Excitedly he told the priest all about how he'd met a man who said he was Jesus at Lime Street, and how he had driven evil spirits out of a woman in a pub. Father Keeley laughed at the young boy's imaginative story, before hurrying on his way.

Tommy's tale was met with a similar reception when he got home. His father, Dominic, warned his son not to follow tramps about, and his mother Christina reeled off a series of grisly tales of child murder, allegedly carried out by vagrants who had befriended children under false pretences. The only person who was open-minded enough to consider the possibility of Jesus being in Liverpool was Tommy's grandmother Patricia, known to her grandson as Nanny Pat. She listened carefully to Tommy's account of the long-haired man in a suit and sandals before relating an intriguing tale of her own.

"Years ago, a woman named Sadie used to mock our family because we were devout churchgoers, and she claimed Jesus had never existed and that the Bible was all made-up nonsense and all that. She worked behind the counter at the big Bon Marché store on Church Street." Her grandson was captivated, and Nanny Pat cleared her throat before continuing. "One day a man came into the store and Sadie noticed he had the most beautiful pair of kind eyes she had ever seen, and he purchased the Holy Bible. She went to wrap it, but he held her hands and stopped her. He said to her, 'It's yours Sadie, please take time to read it.'"

"I've heard this story that many times, I feel as if I was there in person," quipped Mr O'Rourke from behind his newspaper. His wife glared at him with steely blue eyes.

Nanny Pat continued her story. "Anyway, Sadie was taken aback a bit, because she wondered how the mysterious man knew her name. She handed the change to the man, and she saw that he had an open wound in the middle of his palm."

Tommy gasped as he realised what she was saying.

"Sadie felt the wound as she gave him his change, and saw that he had a wound in the other hand too."

"It was Our Lord," said Tommy, his wide eyes revealing that he was full of awe about the possibility.

"Next thing we know, Sadie's joining us for Holy Communion, all hunched up next to me at the altar rail."

Tommy was comforted by the story and felt deep down that there was a lot of truth to the day's incidents. He decided to say nothing more about the unusual man to his family, he was simply pleased that somebody had believed his surreal experience.

A week later, Tommy's grandmother became gravely ill. There was great concern and the family's doctor was called out. Tommy didn't hear what the diagnosis was, but was aware of the doctor speaking to his mother and father in hushed tones. His mother broke down in tears and was led in to the kitchen by the doctor. Tommy knew things were not looking good when Father Keeley was sent for. The priest greeted Nanny Pat at her bedside and seemed pleased that she wore her rosary beads strung around her neck. She had a bottle of holy water on her bedside table. Tommy noticed that the words Father Keeley offered were far from positive. He seemed to be resigned to the old woman's fate. Tommy grew very conscious that he never once assured her that she would make a recovery. Tommy confronted Father Keeley and asked him to try and work a miracle on his grandmother. Once again the priest did not take the boy seriously and he merely patted Tommy's head.

"Jesus raised Lazarus, so why can't you father?" Tommy demanded.

Dominic was astounded at his son's audacity and seized him. He took him into the parlour to slap his legs.

Tommy was distressed and ran out of the house in tears. Desperate for help he began to search for his friend at the Vagrant's Hostel on Shaw Street. Sure enough he found him preaching under the portico to the discards of humanity, and not one of them was laughing or sneering; they were hanging on to every word which the well-spoken spiritual man spoke. When the man spotted his young friend at the bottom of the steps, he curtailed the sermon and went down to meet him. Tommy told him all about his grandmother, who was seriously ill and not expected to live long, and the boy urged the drifter to come and make her better.

The man walked with Tommy to the house in the Dingle, and Mrs O'Rourke was shocked when her son introduced his long-haired friend. She barred his entrance at first, but Tommy started to cry, and begged his mother to admit him so he could save Nanny Pat. If Mr O'Rourke had been at home there would have been blood on the moon, but Tommy's father had just that moment left for work.

The man entered the lobby and Tommy took him up the stairs and straight to his grandmother's room. Nanny Pat looked pale, and made strange gurgling noises as she breathed. Tommy knelt at the bedside and whispered in her ear. He told her that Jesus was here now. He had come from Shaw Street, and was going to perform a miracle on her.

The old lady smiled, and then her eyes turned to look at the visitor.

"Patricia, arise from your sickbed in the name of Jesus. Come forth in the name of Christ!" the man commanded.

Nanny Pat sat up in the bed and began to cough. Tommy grabbed her handkerchief on her pillow and thrust it into her hand. The old woman was captivated by the stranger, and she was shaking slightly, or perhaps trembling in his presence.

Tommy remembered the tale his grandmother had told him about Christ visiting Bon Marché, and he slyly glanced at the man's palm. There was a scar in the centre of his hand! Tommy was now convinced that the man before him was telling the truth.

He asked how she was feeling.

"I just feel like some Guinness," she answered wryly.

Mrs O'Rourke was astounded at her mother's sudden return to health.

"Amen," said the man, and he turned to leave the bedroom.

Mrs O'Rourke could not believe her eyes. She hugged her mother, and asked her repeatedly how she felt. The old woman shrugged off the fuss and carefully made her way back downstairs to sit in her favourite armchair.

The man who had apparently affected a miraculous cure was halfway down the street, when Tommy's mother shouted out to him. She came running down the street desperately thanking him. She offered her hand, and as the miracle man reached out to shake it, she also noticed the curious wound on his palm. She saw no wound on his other palm.

"How can I repay you for my mother's health?" she asked.

The stranger just smiled. "Love the Lord thy God with all of your heart," he said, before turning and leaving.

The doctor called at the house to confirm that Patricia had recovered but still needed some rest. Father Keeley learned of the incident when he also called at the house the next day. He was furious when he heard about the blasphemous confidence trickster who had supposedly cured Patricia with autosuggestion. He vowed to expose him as a fake, and that day sought advice from a senior priest.

A fortnight later, Patricia's friend next door, a seventy-nine-year-old woman named Daisy, fell ill. The outlook was not good, she was expected to die within days. The poor lady had been in and out of the Southern Hospital, but there was nothing the doctors could do for her, so they allowed her to return home to have her final days in familiar surroundings.

Tommy was certain that his new friend could help and told his grandmother so. She decided to listen. The two of them made their way to Shaw Street, but when they reached the Vagrant's Hostel, they found Father Keeley shouting at the man who had cured Tommy's grandmother. A circle of tramps surrounded the two men, and a corpulent, middle-aged policeman stood at the bottom of the steps. Father Keeley announced that he had reported the man "masquerading as Jesus", as he put it. Apparently the authorities were looking for a man matching the description of the mock Christ.

It became apparent that the unruly man's real name was Jeremy Fellowes. He was actually a thirty-three-year-old patient who had escaped from a mental hospital down south. He suffered from schizophrenia and religious mania, and had once tried to crucify himself, but only managed to nail one hand to a plank of wood.

The portly policeman next to Father Keeley stepped forward and grabbed Jeremy by the arm, then led him down the steps and away from the group of onlookers. Tommy and his grandmother rushed forward, and told Jeremy they needed his help. They tried to reason with the policeman, but he would not listen to their excuses.

Jeremy turned to Tommy and his grandmother. His eyes appeared heavy with sorrow. "Tommy, I'm sorry," he murmured looking away sadly. The pained expression on his face told Tommy that he felt he had betrayed his confidence by leading him to believe he really was Jesus.

"I still believe in you," Tommy told him, his mind unswayed by the revelation.

Patricia stepped forward beside Tommy. She pleaded with Jeremy to try and help her dying friend, just as he had helped her.

"Come on, move along, missus," interrupted the policeman abruptly, his patience waring thin. He attempted to push his captive towards the police station round the corner on Prescot Street, when suddenly, Jeremy managed to wriggle free and made a break for it. He took off down the street, with the out of shape policeman trying to give chase but instead ending up out of breath at the end of the street and clutching a stitch in his side.

That night, at precisely nine o'clock, there was a heavy knocking at the O'Rourkes' door. Tommy's mother was surprised to find on her doorstep the man who thought he was Jesus. She was reluctant to let the visitor through, but her mother Patricia invited the escapee in. She led him to the kitchen table and offered him some food and a cup of tea. She asked him earnestly if he would try and cure her friend next door. Jeremy smiled as he answered her and explained that her her recovery had all been down to faith.

Despite Jeremy's reluctance, Patricia managed to persuade him to at least visit her sick friend. At ten o'clock that evening, Jeremy made his way into Daisy's bedroom. He was accompanied by Patricia who was so anxious she clutched his sleeve, and little Tommy was close behind. It was clear to all in the room that the woman lying in bed was seriously ill. As Jeremy sat on the bed, he held on to the fragile lady's hand. Almost unresponsive, she just gazed into his sorrowful eyes with a faraway look.

Patricia was the first to break the intense silence pervading the room.

"It's Jesus, Daisy," she whispered, her tone comforting and calm.

At that moment the police hammered loudly at the front door. Daisy's son went to the door, annoyed that someone could create such a disturbance at the house of such a desperately ill woman. A detective accompanied by three policemen rushed in. It seemed that Father Keeley had alerted the police to the fact that Jeremy had gone into Daisy's home.

The detective stood in the doorway, looking into Daisy's bedroom. He beckoned Jeremy, and the wanted man reluctantly arose from the old woman's deathbed and walked to him with his head bowed.

"How dare you come barging in here when this woman is near death," Patricia whispered to the detective.

"Help me!" groaned Daisy.

Jeremy turned, and moved a pace back towards the old lady. He knelt at her bedside, and held her hand tightly.

"Are you really Jesus?" Daisy asked him faintly.

Jeremy hesitated before replying. "Yes ... I am," he smiled.

"I'm so glad you came for me," said Daisy, her face noticeably eased by his words. The last vestiges of life were fading from her eyes.

"Daisy, this day thou shalt be with me in paradise," Jeremy whispered, with tears in his eyes.

The room was hushed as all eyes fell on Daisy, her face a picture of new found serenity. A vague smile remained on her delicate visage as all signs of life left her.

In what seemed like moments, Jeremy was escorted to the awaiting police car and taken away. Tommy stood close to his grandmother, overwhelmed by the experiences of the last few days. He hugged his grandmother and began to sob.

"There there," Nanny Pat soothed as she rubbed his back. Her wise eyes followed the police car as its headlights faded into the night.

THE VINES CAPER

In Edwardian times, an ingenious theft was planned at the Napoleonic Vaults pub on Copperas Hill. The schemer was an opportunistic thief named Tommy Scott, a slim, slick raven-haired man with a turned-up waxed moustache and a outwardly charming persona. Under false pretences he had landed a job as barman at the Vines public house on the corner of Lime Street and Copperas Hill; a huge premises with a distinctive high tower. This grand baroque pub still stands today.

Tommy was deeply in debt, and to make matters worse, his girlfriend Joan – a maid at the nearby Adelphi Hotel – was pregnant with his child. The thief needed money fast and when he discovered that the landlord of the Vines had a fortune in money and jewellery stashed away in an upstairs safe, he thought that he had found the answer to his prayers. The safe was also where the weekly takings were stored each Thursday night, before being taken to the bank on Friday morning. Tommy was an expert safe cracker, so the only problem was how to escape with the loot once he had opened the safe.

The Vines had old smugglers passages leading from its cellars, leading down to the waterfront. Tommy had explored these passages but found them to be waterlogged and likely to cave in, so they had to be discounted as a possible route to remove the fortune from the pub. Simply dropping the money out of the pub windows down to an accomplice in the street was also unworkable, as both Lime Street and Copperas Hill were always swarming with people, and the beats of four policemen crossed those streets. Tommy Scott therefore laid what he thought was an ingenious plan.

While robbing a house on Edge Lane years before, he had acquired an old crossbow and three bolts, and now he had at last found a use for the archaic weapon. He went to Sefton Park to practise with the crossbow every night for a week, before putting the rather complicated plan into action.

At eleven o'clock, on a Thursday night, there was a stay-behind at the Vines, and as everyone drank behind locked doors, Tommy slipped upstairs and robbed the safe. As he had predicted, that part of the operation was a piece of cake. He then climbed up to the room at the top of the high tower where, earlier, he had hidden the crossbow and bolts. He took careful aim from one of the windows, and fired the crossbow bolt, which was tethered to a long length of fishing line twine. The bolt shot through the open window of the Adelphi hotel bedroom where his accomplice, Joan, was waiting. Joan retrieved the bolt and tied the twine around one of the wooden bedposts. Using the cheap wedding ring he'd bought for Joan, Tommy tied the bag of money to it with wire. The ring was then threaded on to the twine and sent sliding down to the hotel bedroom. At that moment a policeman was strolling down Copperas Hill whistling a tune to himself, and Tommy's heart palpitated, but the policeman didn't look up and carried on his beat.

Then came the hitch, and it was a big hitch. There was a small knot in the twine where it had been tied to another length of twine, but, small though it was, it was enough to stop the wedding ring in its tracks. The policeman passed by, oblivious to what was going on over his head, and then tapped on the Vines windows. Someone opened the pub door and admitted him. Joan shook the twine repeatedly to try and dislodge the ring, but being made of cheap, base metal, it broke under the weight of the loot! The fortune went crashing into the street, at the exact place where an old man named Coots was staggering into the pub to join the stay-behind. Ironically, this same man Coots had been conned out of some money by Tommy just a week ago.

It took a short while for the startled Coots to assess the situation. He swayed to and fro gormlessly eyeing the mysterious package which had landed at his feet. Eventually, he mustered up the co-ordination to pick up the bag and opened it. Even in his befuddled state he was able to put two and two together and he hammered loudly on the window of the Vines. Tommy Scott ran downstairs intending to make his escape through the back yard, but he could hear a tremendous commotion in the bar. Coots had already been admitted into the pub and was busy spreading the contents of the bag along the bar. All the late night customers and the policeman who had called in for a warming tot of whisky, crowded round as wads of money and gold and jewels were fished out of the bag. The landlord was shocked to see his fortune and all his wife's jewellery spread out along the bar. How could it possibly have got there?

The mystery was soon solved when Tommy Scott was caught red-handed trying to sneak out of the back gate. He was arrested and charged by the policeman and ended up doing three years' hard labour for the crime.

Ironically, Tommy Scott overlooked the real fortune that was hanging on the walls of the Vines – two paintings – by the artist George Earl, which were worth a fortune had anyone realised their true value. Their worth was eventually recognised in the 1990s, and they were purchased for seven hundred and fifty thousand pounds.

THE HYPOCHONDRIAC

One pleasant August evening in 1882, Bob Clock, a cab driver of Everton Brow, sat coughing loudly atop his hansom cab, a vehicle that cost him twelve shillings a day to hire. The gas lamps of Lime Street shone their steady yellow light through the purple shades of dusk, and a full harvest moon blazed its silvery radiance over Brownlow Hill. The tail of Jack, the old horse who pulled the hansom cab, started to flick as Nellie, the shamrock seller and occasional flower girl approached with a titbit for him, given to her by the costermongers. Most evenings, the impoverished but charismatic Nellie could procure something from the costers, and she always brought something for Bob's arthritic horse, of whom she was very fond.

Jack munched the carrot, and Bob and Nellie exchanged small talk as a tall, elegantly-dressed man in a top hat, cape, white gloves and carrying a cane, came out of the Adelphi Hotel. He hailed Bob Clock, and entered the hansom, mumbling distractedly to himself. Bob slid back the small panel in the roof of the cab and looked down at the distinguished passenger.

"Where to, governor?"

"Anywhere for now," said Victor Spurstow, a well known eccentric millionaire.

"Anywhere?" repeated Bob, somewhat nonplussed by the vague instructions.

"Yes, anywhere and everywhere!" Spurstow shouted, "I want to see more of my hometown before I die, which shan't be long from now."

Bob drove the hansom up Renshaw Street, into Berry Street and through the Chinatown quarter into the purlieus of the night-time city, on a meandering journey towards the waterfront. A long hour passed, and while in transit, Spurstow suddenly hammered his gloved fist on the roof of the hansom and opened the small trapdoor.

"Stop, man! Let us wait here for a while!" Victor Spurstow yelled.

The hansom cab trundled to a halt at the quayside of one of the docks. The millionaire and the cabbie climbed out and stood looking at the misty shroud cloaking the river, and the swaying forest of the sailing ships' spars silhouetted against the distant twinkling lamps of Wirral. Spurstow rambled on about the rare illness from which he was suffering, and how all the eminent physicians he had consulted had accused him, in the politest possible way, of being a hypochondriac.

"But what about this lump? Is this imaginary?" asked Spurstow, pointing to his Adam's apple.

Bob soon realised that the gentleman was obsessed with illness and fixated with morbid thoughts about death. Spurstow had already had his own marble tomb constructed, and was in the process of drawing up a will. As he was reflecting upon his impending demise, he asked Bob if he should like to be included in the will. Bob answered that all he required was his payment for the cab fare. Spurstow promised that he would pay up, and give a generous tip to boot, once they had arrived back at the Adelphi.

Spurstow then produced a silver drinking flask from his hip pocket and unscrewed its top. He took a small swig, and studied the pale sails of the vessels coming down the Mersey. He offered Bob the flask, and Bob obligingly took a swig of the expensive brandy. Being a true hypochondriac, Spurstow then refused to drink further out of the flask because he feared coming into contact with the cabman's germs. He put the flask back in his pocket, intending to decontaminate it at some future time.

Back at the Adelphi, Victor Spurstow duly paid Bob, and gave him a whole sovereign as a tip. He also promised the cabby that, despite his protestations, he would be included in his will. Bob laughed, convinced in his heart that the hypochondriacal millionaire would outlive him by decades, for he looked as fit as a flea. However, five months later, Spurstow died after a short illness of the lungs that was thought to have been tuberculosis. The doctors were baffled as to how he had contracted the disease, as their patient was obsessed with looking after his health and had always eaten the best of everything. Yet, somehow, it seemed as if a potent microbe had managed to penetrate the millionaire's robust immune system.

The executor of the will informed the humble cabbie that he was to receive the massive sum of ten thousand pounds. Meanwhile, Bob Clock had a grim suspicion that when he had sipped from Spurstow's brandy flask, he had left germs on the lip of the container which the millionaire had probably inadvertently drunk from afterwards, forgetting that he had shared it with the cabbie. The cabby had never had his long-term cough investigated by a doctor, and maybe he was unwittingly a carrier of the deadly tuberculosis germ.

Being a simple man, Bob did not dwell long on the whys and wherefores of his good fortune. Instead he made very good use of his new-found wealth and bought a number of hansom cabs and soon became quite the entrepreneur. He also remembered his friends and gave Nellie the shamrock seller enough money to buy her own home.

STRANGE CREATURES AT LARGE

THE BIRD THAT PREYED ON PEOPLE

Across the world there have been reports of unusual creatures that do not fit into the surroundings in which they are spotted. These so-called 'out-of-place animals' include the Surrey Puma, the Beast of Bodmin, the Loch Ness Monster, Morgawr the surviving dinosaur, the Yeti, the Abominable Snowman, and the universal oversized Black Dog. Not only are there mysterious out-of-place animals roaming the world, there are many undiscovered species of creatures that biologists and entomologists know nothing about. Take, for example, the elusive species of giant bird that has allegedly been seen in Europe, North America, South America, and many other places in the world. In 1838, the respected scientist FA Pouchet documented a reported encounter with one of these huge birds in Valais, Switzerland:

A little girl, five years old, called Marie Delex, was playing with one of her companions on a mossy slope of the mountains, when all at once an eagle swooped down upon her and carried her away in spite of the cries and presence of her young friend.

Some peasants, hearing the screams, hastened to the spot, but sought in vain for the child, for they found nothing but one of her shoes on the edge of a precipice.

The child, however, was not carried to the eagle's nest, where only two eaglets were seen, surrounded by heaps of goat and sheep bones.

It was not till two months after this that a shepherd discovered the corpse of Marie Delex, frightfully mutilated, and lying upon a rock, half a league from where she had been carried off.

Ornithologists treated the report of the giant bird of the Alps as a far-fetched tale. The bird experts argued that no known bird had claws strong enough to carry off a small child. However, the winged monster that carried off Marie Delex must have been an unknown bird, and in the decades following the bizarre tragedy in the Alps, there were many more reports of giant birds carrying off pigs, lambs and other livestock.

In 1868, an enormous bird swooped down on an eight-year-old boy named Jemmie Kenney in Tippah County, Missouri. His teacher was alerted to the terrifying child-snatching bird by his screaming pupils, but when he looked up, he saw that the bird was so high, if it dropped Jemmie he'd be killed.

As the children stared up in horror, the giant bird released its screaming prey, and he plummeted to his death. When the teacher looked upon the boy's broken body in a field, he saw that the talons of the bird had dug deep into Jemmie's back and stomach.

Strangely enough, American Indian lore in that area mentions 'Thunderbirds' – huge creatures with enormous wingspans that made a sound like thunder when they flapped their wings.

Here in Liverpool I have received many reports over the years from readers concerning a huge black bird of prey, resembling a giant crow, which has been seen swooping down out of the skies over Sefton Park. Most of the sightings of the bird have been at the edge of day, when twilight is descending. One man walking his dog in the park one evening in 1997 described how he saw a gigantic bird. The creature was walking with a waddling gait behind several trees. The man's dog barked, and the bird stretched its six-foot-long wings and took off across the lake. It headed in the direction of Mossley Hill.

THE THING IN THE CHUTE

The most chilling tale of an unidentified creature in Liverpool has to be the Thing In the Chute – a creepy story that was related to me many years ago. In 1968, a twelve-year-old child named Theresa, whose family lived on the third floor of the Gerard Gardens tenements in Liverpool, was emptying a small bin down the wall refuse chute, when she suddenly let out a high-pitched scream and ran back to her home in a terrible state.

Her right hand was cut at the knuckles, apparently by a razor blade, because the wound was clean, straight and thin, and about four inches in length. However, Theresa tearfully claimed that 'something horrible' had inflicted the wound. This creature, which the girl could hardly bear to describe, had a small long grey head, shaped like the head of a snake, but its eyes were just small lumps, and Theresa thought it looked as though it was blind.

Apparently, when the girl had pulled the wall chute's cast iron cover back, the head of the creature had darted out and bitten down hard on her knuckle. Reflexively, Theresa had withdrawn her hand from the chute, and as she did so, the creature's sharp fang had been drawn across the knuckle, causing the razor-like slash.

Theresa's parents were concerned that their child had imagined the monster in the chute, but over the next few weeks, several other people living in the flats around Theresa's home also saw something strange coming in and out of the chute on the landings of the tenement.

An old woman who was emptying her bin down the chute early one morning heard a strange clicking sound to her left, and when she turned to look down along the landing, she saw something that sent her running indoors in a petrified state. A long grey creature, with a snake-like body about five feet in length, was hurrying towards the woman on six thin black spidery legs. The three pairs of legs were spaced evenly along the thin body, and were positioned by the head, the tail and halfway down the body. Each leg terminated in a hideous single hooked claw, and these claws scratched the floor and made the clicking sounds as the creature scuttled down the landing.

The old woman told a neighbour about the strange legged snake she had seen, and he took an hatchet from the old coal cupboard in the hallway and went to hunt for the bizarre-looking creature, but found nothing amiss inside the chute.

A week later, three women were standing on the third-floor landing in Gerard Gardens one evening, talking and gossiping, when one of them noticed that the chute cover had been left open, and the putrid-smelling aroma of decay was drifting from it. The woman then noticed a small pointed head emerge from the chute and she screamed, because she was convinced that the thing was a rat. Jimmy, the woman's son, fetched a torch and shone it down the chute, but recoiled in horror when he saw a creature's head and its upper body in the darkness.

The thing made a loud hissing sound when the torch was shone upon it, and Jimmy was so scared he slammed the chute cover shut and told his mother that it wasn't a rat at all but some weird looking and threatening snake.

A short while later, a refuse collector was emptying the large communal metal bin at the bottom of the chute, when he noticed something grey dangling down from the end of it. With his gloved hand he seized what he thought was a discarded length of rubber hose, when he heard a blood-curdling screech above his head. Vile-looking yellow liquid jelly dripped down, and the bin-man hurled the revolting grey twitching piece of tubing into the bin. The rubbish was then transferred to the wagon.

After that final strange incident, the hideous Thing in the Chute was seen no more.

IF WALLS COULD TALK

One cold Sunday afternoon in October 1908, Colonel Travers' Empire Band was giving an inspiring recital of 'The Dashing White Sergeant' on the bandstand in Newsham Park, when there was a commotion amongst the audience. A large red parrot was circling low above the brass band, and it was being chased by a delta formation of about twelve wood pigeons. The distressed parrot's droppings fell on the uniforms of several members of the Colonel's brass band and the audience, and the exotic bird also squawked and let out a string of swearwords, before fluttering away to the north of the park.

The same red parrot, with its accompanying squadron of wood pigeons, was seen circling Newsham Park aviary some minutes later, causing the caged birds to suddenly go crazy, flying into the wire of their cages and making a tremendous din. The parrot was then chased across the sky by the pigeons until it flew straight through the open window of a large house on Newsham Drive where the McRobie family lived.

James Allan McRobie, a well-to-do businessman, had been reading a newspaper in his drawing room when the crimson-feathered parrot fluttered through the curtains and landed on the marble mantelpiece. It threw back its head, opened its beak and started to screech with what sounded like manic laughter.

James McRobie jumped to his feet and rolled up his newspaper, intending to swat the deranged parrot back towards the window, because from the instant he had set eyes upon the bird, he received the distinct impression that it was something evil. However, before James could take a swipe at the parrot, his wife Julianne entered the drawing room and stared in puzzlement at the bird.

"The damn thing flew in here just now," her husband explained, pointing towards the open window where the heavy brocade curtains were stirring in the breeze.

Just a fortnight before, Julianne's old parakeet, of which she was very fond, had died, and she immediately thought that the stray parrot would make a fine replacement. So she hurried to the window and closed it, then told her husband to fetch the cage in which the parakeet had lived.

"I'm not so sure," said James. "I don't like the look of that thing."

He wasn't keen on the idea of having the red parrot as a pet in the household, but he couldn't say why, because his wife would think he was being silly if he said that he felt it was somehow evil.

Julianne was in no mood for arguments, being used to always getting her own way, and she cajoled her husband by reminding him how sad she had been since the death of her beloved pet. She repeated her request for him to fetch the cage from the garret. James sighed and shook his head, but nevertheless did as he was asked. She then leaned towards the parrot with an affectionate smile.

"What's your name then?" she asked.

The tropical feathered creature suddenly lost its voice and instead fixed her with its beady eyes. Julianne was a little unnerved by its gaze and decided not to risk tickling it beneath the chin as she used to do with her own parakeet, and she put the parrot's implacable gaze down to distress.

However, the bird was soon installed in the tall cage and seemed quite at home on its perch, from where it kept a beady eye on everything that went on. It seemed to be enjoying all the attention being lavished upon it by Julianne and it found its voice once more and began copying all the phrases uttered by the McRobie family.

However, a few weeks later, the parrot – named Bruce by Julianne – caused a blazing row one evening when, out of the blue, it squawked, "Christopher, I love you."

Mr McRobie's eyes immediately turned from the financial pages of his newspaper to the cheeky parrot who he still regarded with deep suspicion. He cursed his weakness for giving in to Julianne and allowing the feathered intruder into his house – was he a man or a mouse? On this occasion, the parrot's words struck a chord. He was well aware of its power of mimicry and thought it was a strange thing for the parrot to utter. He then recalled how a certain neighbour named Christopher Moody had been amorously eyeing Julianne at a recent church fete. His suspicions roused, he made a mental note to watch Julianne very closely over the next few days, and he took particular notice of everything the parrot said. It was not long before his suspicions were confirmed and one evening the police were called to the McRobies' house to investigate reports of a loud altercation between the couple. It transpired that the red parrot had once again shattered the domestic peace of the household with an even more inflammatory remark. On this occasion the accursed bird had squawked, "Oh, Christopher, make love to me, darling!"

Julianne had stood by blushing deeply and looking aghast; a reaction which confirmed her guilty secret.

Enough was enough. In a jealous rage, James Allan McRobie struck his wife across the face, knocking her out cold. He then strode across the room to the birdcage, intending to wring the accursed parrot's neck, but it was then that he got the shock of his life. The bird had somehow managed to bend the bars of the cage and was now flitting about the room, chuckling a sinister laugh, and taunting Mr McRobie about his marital problems by repeating the hateful phrases.

Snatching up the nearest object to him, McRobie hurled an antique vase at the parrot, but it missed the bird and instead smashed the window, landing in pieces in the shrubbery. Never one to miss a trick, the parrot seized its opportunity and flew to freedom through the hole in the window pane.

McRobie was neither a religious nor superstitious man, but he became convinced that the mischievous red parrot had been some kind of agent of Satan.

DOPPELGANGERS

THE LORD STREET DOPPELGANGER

In November 1930, a trio of navvies stood near the kerb on Southport's Lord Street. One particular worker was down on one knee, holding an iron spike in position, while the other two men were poised to strike the head of the spike with fifteen-pound sledgehammers.

The two hammer men would take turns to strike the spike in rapid succession, and then they would loosen the spike by hitting it side-on. This was a dying ritual in those days for digging a hole in the road to gain access to a suspected burst pipe.

Upon this snowy November day, the man holding the spike was a fifty-six-year-old Welshman named Glyn Hughes, and by law he should have been holding the spike with a long pair of tongs, but there was a foolish tradition of holding the spike with the fingers in a macho manner. The first hammer struck the pin forcefully, then the second hammer drove it even further, and the alternating hammer strikes were watched by the shoppers on Lord Street.

All of a sudden, Glyn Hughes seemed startled by something in the crowd of bystanders, and at the moment of his distraction, one of the fifteen-pound sledgehammers was deflected by the spike's head. It crashed into the tarmac with the Welshman's thumb under it. Women screamed in the crowd of horrified onlookers, and several people ran forward to help the injured man, who was holding his flattened and bloody thumb with a mixture of absolute agony and disbelief on his face.

As Glyn was escorted into a nearby café, one of the hammer men asked the Welshman what exactly had distracted him.

"Didn't you see him?" he asked timidly.

"See who, Glyn?" the hammer man enquired.

Glyn turned, and pointed with his uninjured hand to a man among the spectators. His face had grown pale.

The hammer man gasped in amazement, because that bystander was a man who was the exact replica of Glyn Hughes. He had exactly the same face and portly build. He wore the same fawn coloured cloth cap, the same dark green coarse flannel shirt, corduroy trousers with leather straps around the knees, and hobnail boots.

"I don't like that," said Glyn, as he was bundled into the café. "He looks like a wraith."

The double stood there gazing at its counterpart with a blank expression, while everyone else's eyes followed the nauseating trail of blood leading from the hole in the road into the café.

In the café, a waitress brought a first aid kit to the table and bandaged the injured thumb, while a businessman offered to take Glyn to hospital in his car. Glyn stared out the window at the eerie double, and watched him walk away slowly down Lord Street.

That week, Glyn Hughes suddenly decided to make out a will at a solicitor's office in which he left his savings to his wife, from whom he was separated. He then made three visits to old friends whom he'd had longstanding feuds with, and buried the hatchet with each of them. He told his landlady at his lodging house in Birkdale that she'd be able to let his room soon because his end was near. She thought he was just depressed, but he explained to her that three members of his family in Wales had died shortly after seeing their own wraiths, or doubles rather. He explained to the landlady that in Wales, a superstitious tradition held that if a man met his ghostly twin – known as a doppelganger – he would die soon afterwards.

That had certainly been the case with his own family, and the doppelganger curse stretched back generations.

Five days later, Glyn Hughes died in his sleep from natural causes. I've written about doppelgangers before, and the Glyn Hughes case is an uncommon occurrence of death following a doppelganger sighting, so if you happen to see your own double in the street – even if it is wearing the same clothes – do not assume that your death is imminent. Most people who see their doppelgangers come to no harm whatsoever, they merely suffer from strained nerves!

ELVIS' DOPPELGANGER

In 1973 Tony Evans from Liverpool went on a caravanning holiday with his Scottish wife Agnes to Aberdeenshire. They found a caravan site buried away deep in the countryside and they pitched their caravan. That evening the couple visited an old tavern in the village of Lonmay, and ended up drinking until nearly three in the morning at the stay-behind, or lock-in, as some people like to call them.

When they finally left the pub it was dark and they hadn't thought to bring a torch, forgetting that they were no longer in the city and that there would be no street lights. Tony and Agnes staggered along the road which they were sure would lead them to the caravan site, but they lost their way and ended up in the middle of the countryside with not a house or a light in sight and only the moon to guide them.

Eventually, after wandering about aimlessly for over an hour, they came upon what they thought was an old barn, and they could just make out a faint flickering fire inside the building.

As they walked nearer to the barn, they could hear the rhythmic clanging of metal being struck, and when they walked into the building, they realised that it was a blacksmith's shop. A man with his back to them was busy hammering a glowing orange horseshoe on an anvil, and he obviously wasn't aware that the couple were behind him.

Tony called out, and the blacksmith slowly turned towards them. Straight away, the couple were struck by the blacksmith's handsome appearance – the glossy black quiff ... the smouldering eyes ... the full lips ... were all very familiar for some reason. At first they thought the man just resembled some famous actor, but then they suddenly recognised the all-too-familiar face which, out of context, they hadn't been able to place, and became speechless. The man had coal black hair, with long thick sideburns and was unmistakeably Elvis Presley.

But it didn't make sense; what was Elvis doing at a blacksmith's forge at that hour of the morning in Scotland? The man mopped his brow and talked in a thick Scottish accent that Tony's girlfriend could barely understand. The Elvis doppelganger glared at the visitors still wielding a huge hammer in his hand. The couple didn't stop to ask questions, but backed away, then ran off at full pelt into the night.

They looked for landmarks and noted where the blacksmith's shop was before setting off again in search of the campsite. They eventually found the campsite but had little sleep that night.

As soon as they had had breakfast the following morning, they set off in search of the bizarre, all-night forge. In daylight it was much easier to navigate their way in the unfamiliar countryside and they were able to retrace their steps by looking for the landmarks they had specially noted. They arrived at the field without any problem, but there was no sign of a barn, or indeed of anything unusual, at that location.

The couple made enquiries around the village of Lonmay, and learned that there was no blacksmith anywhere near the area of the field. The village blacksmith was a tubby, old, grey-haired man who worked on the other side of Lonmay village.

The couple did learn however, that other people had seen the ghostly blacksmith at his forge over the years. A publication called *Weekend* magazine printed the story, and the strange tale eventually reached the United States, and Elvis Presley himself heard about the weird incident. Elvis was fascinated by ghosts and all things supernatural, and it was said that, after he had heard about the ghostly blacksmith, he secretly hired experts in the field of genealogy to research his ancestry.

Incredibly, the experts discovered that Elvis Presley's ancestral home was a remote Scottish hamlet in Aberdeenshire – called Lonmay. A blacksmith called Andrew Presley had married Elspeth Leg in Lonmay on 27 August 1713. Their son, also named Andrew, became the first Presley in America when he arrived in North Carolina in 1745.

The unanswered question then is this: did Tony Evans and his girlfriend see the ghost of Andrew Presley – ancestor of the King himself – that night in Lonmay?

TIME TRAVEL

The poorly understood power of time can be very destructive, as we all know. In its subtle passing it can ravage the most aesthetically beautiful face, corrode and topple the greatest building, and could ultimately bring the earth's rotation to a gradual halt (through tidal friction); but what exactly is time?

Professor Stephen Hawking – the foremost expert on time and space in modern times – as well as Albert Einstein, have formulated elaborate theories regarding time, yet their conjectures have not yet provided us with a practical way to control the passing of time, or to allow one of the human race's age-old dreams to come true: the ability to travel into the past and future.

The prophetic Victorian writer HG Wells wrote a novel called *The Time Machine* in 1895, in which an amateur scientist builds a vehicle that travels thousands of years into the future. Wells explained to his readers that there are three dimensions of space: backwards and forwards (length), side-to-side (breadth) and up and down (depth). All of these dimensions are at right angles to one another, but the fourth dimension – the dimension of time – stood apart.

Albert Einstein came to this same conclusion in his theories of Relativity in the early twentieth century, but HG Wells beat him to it. Wells stated that we can specify 'where' a physical object is with the three spatial co-ordinates of length, breadth and depth, but to specify 'when' an object is, we have to use the entirely separate co-ordinates of the time dimension. For example, the position of a person in Liverpool can be specified by 53.25 degrees latitude and three degrees longitude, but to be completely accurate, we would have to say when that person was there (ie 16 October 1968 at 10.15pm, for example).

So much for the dimensions of space and time; what about the phenomenon of timewarps? A timewarp is when an element of the past or future intrudes into the present.

A VOICE FROM THE FUTURE

In 1992, Billy Wilson, of Aigburth, experienced an intriguing timewarp concerning what appeared to be radio messages from the future, and these cross-time transmissions were apparently from Billy himself! The time was 5am, and the place was the office of Merseycabs, off London Road. Billy was sitting at the microphone when suddenly, a faint but familiar voice came over the speakers.

"Who's the next cab on the Kingsley Road stand?" said the voice.

Billy was dumbfounded, because he immediately recognised it as his own voice. He listened tensely, and heard his voice ask another question.

"Who's on Penny Lane?" it said.

Several more messages came in mentioning Broadway and other

locations in the city, all in Billy's own distinctive voice. Then the baffling transmissions ceased as abruptly as they had started.

"It was so uncanny," said fifty-five-year-old Billy, who has now retired from Merseycabs and runs the Calderstones Café in Calderstones Park. "Hearing my own voice broadcast to the cabs – it was weird. An hour later, a list of jobs came up on the computer, and as I read them off over the radio, I realised they were the very same ones I'd heard earlier on the radio. I mentioned Kingsley Road, Penny Lane, Broadway, and so on. It was as if something had given me a preview of the future, and it still baffles me to this day."

THE UNEXPLAINED URCHIN

The idea of what we call 'time' is one of the most fundamental yet baffling concepts tackled by the human mind. Even the most down to earth person has, at some time in his or her life, suspected that there is more to time than meets the eye. Albert Einstein, Stephen Hawking and other gifted physicists have forever altered the way we used to think of time, and nowadays, concepts such as parallel universes, hyperspace, timewarps, and faster-than-light travel, are no longer found within science fiction books, but within accepted textbooks of physics. The following two cases which came my way via several readers, seem to suggest that there is a possibility that people from other eras may sometimes intrude into our time period. The first story was related to me back in the 1990s when I was a regular guest on the Billy and Wally Show on Radio City.

The Mathew Street Cavern Walks complex of shops, clubs, pubs, restaurants and cafés opened in 1984, and replaced rows of old warehouses, many of which dated back to Victorian times. Award-winning architect David Backhouse was responsible for the Royal Insurance Company's development of Cavern Walks, which is now a major tourist attraction and highly popular shopping destination for visitors to the city as well as local people. However, most people who shop in the brightly lit fashionable arcades and attractive shops of Cavern Walks are not aware of a strange supernatural incident that took place when two rows of old warehouses were being demolished and renovated to make way for the Mathew Street development.

Around 1982, construction workers in one of the warehouses destined to become a major part of Cavern Walks spotted a shabbily dressed child of about ten years of age, walking around in his barefeet on the upper floors of the building. Two builders who noticed the child grew concerned as the area was far from safe. They went upstairs to try and find the minor, but were left perplexed when they discovered that the child had completely vanished into thin air. What made both men shudder was the fact that all of the windows on the upper floors were securely barred and had been for decades. There were no possible exits the boy could have used to leave the building, without having to pass the men first.

The same ragged-looking little boy was spotted on many more occasions, both at day and night. He was observed by scaffolders, electricians, security men, and other people working on the warehouses. What was more distinctive was that the child was always seen coming from one particular part of the warehouse and it was at that specific point where an intriguing discovery was made.

One evening, a security man challenged the suspicious boy after catching a glimpse of him crouched down low and attempting to pick up a reel of heavy duty electrical copper wire which one of the builders had left out for the next day's work.

Around that time, the reports of the boy at large in the development area were thought to be sightings of a ghost, but the security officer who had actually bumped into the boy and had tried to grab him, knew that the child was a solid flesh and blood boy and not some ethereal being. The boy was chased into a former storage room, and at the end of this room, the child ran straight through the wall. The security officer, who I shall refer to as David, could only watch in sheer disbelief. The beam of his powerful torch played over the bricks of the wall which the boy had passed through. The guard eased over to the wall until he was up close and could touch the bricks. He was amazed as his hand passed right through them like swiping his hand through fresh air. It was as if the bricks weren't there.

David was naturally shocked, and quickly he began to doubt his senses. With his torch scouring the now deserted room, the security man prodded at the bricks that were no more substantial than air. Suddenly, the head of the flashlight passed into the wall with effortless penetration. David withdrew the torch with a jerky reaction and then attempted to push it through the bricks again, only to hear it clunk heavily. Somehow the wall had now returned to its normal solidity.

Having a sound mind was mandatory for a security officer, there was no time for fanciful ideas and overreactions when protecting premises, so David decided to tell no one about the bizarre invisible hole in the wall, although he did decide to conduct his own night-time investigations into its true nature.

One evening, David was investigating the mysterious wall that had baffled him so much. He felt around for a moment and then bravely thrust his hand – which held a small camera – through the bricks, just at the point when their density seemed to become non-existent. After clicking the camera button, he quickly snatched his hand and the camera from beyond the wall. He managed to perform this action twice more, before the wall returned to its more normal state. What is more, the unusual 'hole' in it never appeared again, or at least it never recurred while David patrolled the warehouse.

David hypothesised that the odd little phantom child who had been seen at the warehouse so many times, had in fact been a street urchin from Victorian days who had perhaps discovered a hole in time and space in his own day and age, and had passed through it to gain access to 1982, where he had stolen various items at the modern-day warehouse. The theory did make a lot of sense, as tools and various items had gone missing from the warehouse after dark when it was securely locked. David wondered if these purloined objects had been taken by a ragged-trousered time-travelling boy who had taken advantage of the unusual gateway through time.

THE DESERTED YARD

In the Anfield district of Liverpool in 1997, a forty-six-year-old woman named Margaret left her home on Heyes Street at 3.30pm. She made her way to Breck Road, where she planned to buy cigarettes and a magazine. After purchasing her goods, she started to near home about fifteen minutes later, and noticed how dark the skies had grown. It was early August, and yet all of a sudden the heaviness of the overbearing sky made it seem like a late January afternoon. Margaret took a short cut to her house via the alleyway, near to a public house called The Midden, and when she opened the backyard gate of her home, she froze. Standing around in her yard were five children, each dressed in seemingly old-fashioned clothes. Three of the children were boys, dressed in brown short pants that were worn and in need of repairing. Two of them wore cloth caps, and were dressed quite poorly. The two girls with them also wore threadbare faded clothes, and these girls and one of the boys were bare-footed.

Margaret experienced an instinctive sensation that the children were ghosts, not just because of their outdated and poverty-stricken looks, but also because of their deathly pallid faces. Margaret edged backwards and carefully pulled against the backyard door until she heard the latch snap shut again.

She hurried to her younger sister's house round the corner on Rydal Street. When Margaret explained to her sister Karen about the ghostly children in the backyard, she expected her story to be met with some disbelief. This was not the case. Apparently, a few days before, Karen's daughter Becky had returned home somewhat distressed. She had noticed a boy in a cloth cap and worn-looking clothes near to her house. The ragamuffin had followed her down an alleyway on her way home from school. At one point, Becky had grown uncomfortable and ran off, only to find that the outdated boy gave chase, laughing out loud as he did so. The frightened schoolgirl had reached her home in a dreadful state, even though her paranormal pursuer had vanished somewhere back in the alleyway.

When Margaret heard this she felt unable to return to her home until later that evening. At 9pm, her brother-in-law Tony gave her a lift home and checked the backyard for her. Dismissing any such ideas of ghosts, he reassured Margaret that the yard was empty. There was definitely no one there, however the backyard door was found to be wide open.

Over the next couple of months there were many more sightings of the eerie impoverished children in the alleyways of Heyes Street, but the hauntings ended as suddenly as they had started, and no one knows what caused the ghosts to walk in the first place.

SHADOW ENTITIES

A SINISTER BLACK SHADOW FALLS

Asoft night wind stirred a teenaged girl's long black hair as she sat on a bench on Speke Boulevard. In her hand she clasped a can of lager. Her two male friends were both aged about fourteen. The lads were smoking, as they periodically swigged vodka from the plastic soft drinks bottles. The boys had an arrogance about them, convinced that their underage drinking was well disguised.

A further group of teenage girls gathered on the secluded stretch of the Boulevard, and the rowdy bunch of underage smokers and drinkers laughed and argued and boasted among themselves. There was all the usual tom foolery associated with such gatherings, including offensive gesturing at passers-by and traffic.

It was a sight Craig was sick of seeing through the closed-circuit television cameras of the factory at which he worked each long and tedious night. Most mornings at one o'clock, a fellow security guard named Ken came into the room to break the monotony with a pot noodle or a pack of sandwiches, and he would also look at the images of the juvenile delinquents on the monitor screens of the security surveillance room.

Weekends and the school holidays were the worst, when gangs of kids reaching numbers of up to thirty or more would rampage on the Boulevard, and the police cautions and patrols seemed to do nothing to deter the wild children from their antisocial antics. They continued to congregate near the factory, often scaling the fences and sitting on the walls surrounding it. Craig had asked the factory owners to attempt some kind of deterrent such as topping the walls and gates with barbed wire and anti-vandalism grease, but the guard's requests were never responded to.

In June 1998, Craig was at the bank of monitors, manipulating the remote-controlled cameras. A radio was turned down low in the background, churning out a tinny echo of music. As he observed all of the focused areas, he caught a glimpse of something that chilled him to the bone and set the hairs on his neck on end. Some kind of shadow moved rapidly from the darkness at the side of a building and flitted into another patch of blackness in the space of a second. The dark penumbra seemed to stretch and disguise itself as the angular shadow of a shed when it reached its destination.

On the monitor, Craig could see Ken walking through the yard and straight towards where this unidentifiable dark 'thing' was lurking. As soon as the security guard passed through the yard and turned a corner, the shadow of the shed peeled itself quickly off the ground, and appeared to slide up the wall, before vanishing over it.

The unusual sighting all happened so fast, Craig just sat there, gazing at the monitor, trying to take it in and make some sense of the puzzling phenomenon. After a moment's pause, he lifted his radio transceiver and spoke into it. At first his voice was caught. Still unnerved, Craig cleared his throat and attempted to speak again.

"Ken, come up here a moment," he demanded, with a note of urgency in his voice.

Ken acknowledged the request and entered the monitor room. He found Craig analysing the screens with a disconcerting expression on his face. Craig turned to face him and explained what he had seen as accurately as he could, more than aware of how bizarre his experience sounded. Indeed, Ken was more than a little sceptical, until Craig rewound the security camera tape and played it back for his colleague.

Watched at normal speed, the mysterious shadow was so fleeting in its movements, that Craig had to replay it several times so Ken could see what he was talking about. However, when the tape was played at a slower speed, the shadowy entity looked even more sinister and was more easily visible. Ken and Craig agreed that the black shape was definitely not some trick of the light or an optical illusion; it was some sort of amorphous black entity that displayed an intelligence of some kind.

When Ken saw himself walk past the entity on the television monitor, he shuddered and turned cold.

"What could it be?" Craig asked, as he rewound and replayed the tape again and again, frame by frame.

Over the next month, the menacing shade was not only captured by the closed-circuit television cameras, it was seen by Ken at close quarters, and the experience really shook him up. The frightening encounter took place at 3.20am one Thursday morning in July 1998. Ken was walking down a narrow passage between two buildings near the perimeter walls of the factory yards, when he saw what looked like a black ground mist rolling towards him. He quickly realised that it was the eerie shadow he'd seen in the footage of the TV security cameras. Ken turned on his heels and ran to a nearby hut, where he stayed for half an hour, until he was sure that the dark cloud had gone.

The most chilling incident concerning the vaporous being took place days later, when Craig was once again at the bank of monitors, checking and rechecking the screens, when suddenly he noticed a solitary girl, aged about thirteen or fourteen, staggering past the front gates of the factory with a small bottle in her hand.

The girl was violently sick, and she threw down the bottle, smashing it into pieces all over the ground, before tottering away up the road. The teenaged girl didn't get far before she fell flat on her face. Craig zoomed the camera in on her and alerted Ken and another guard named Robbie to the collapsed teenager. The guards made a beeline to the gate, and as Ken left the factory to tend to the girl, Robbie telephoned the paramedics and the police. Ken ran down the lonely, poorly lit lane, then turned a corner. He shone his flashlight at the girl – and saw that the shadow entity was covering her. The murky life form was star shaped now and spread across the unconscious girl, who was shivering, as if she was having a seizure.

Of course, people under extreme stress behave out of character. Ken panicked and let out a string of expletives before charging at the shape. The murky entity darted away from the girl and crossed Speke Boulevard, where it melted into the darkness of a field. Minutes later, Robbie joined Ken at the scene and shortly afterwards, an ambulance arrived. The girl was taken to hospital and her stomach was pumped, because she had taken unidentified pills and washed them down with scotch after having a row with her mother. Luckily, she later made a full recovery.

The shadow was seen no more at the factory in Speke, but in 2004 I was giving a talk at Woolton Hall, when a young man approached me with a videotape. He said he was a security guard at a factory in Speke – not the same one where Craig, Ken and Robbie worked – and he told me that something very strange had been captured by a closed circuit television camera at his factory. The guard wanted my opinion on what the thing that had been captured on camera could possibly be.

I viewed the tape with natural curiosity when I got home, and found it to be a large shadow that was moving around in some loading bay at a factory complex, and the thing appeared to be mimicking the shadows of buildings. I am sure the black cloud-like entity is the very same one that haunted the other factory in Speke, but just what it is I cannot say. I still have a video cassette that shows the shadow on the move. Sometimes I wonder if these unearthly entities come from some crack between our world and another one that is separated by a wafer thin dimension of space and time.

I shudder when I think what would have happened to the prostrate, unconscious teenager, had Ken not challenged the vaporous fiend.

SHADOW OF DOOM

The shadow entity in Speke is reminiscent of a similar incident that allegedly took place at the Royal Liverpool Hospital on Pembroke Place in Edwardian Liverpool. A man named Charles Shaw was recovering from a serious operation. His hospital bed was situated at the end of a ward which contained seven beds. Mr Shaw suffered from insomnia, unable to sleep due to his extreme pain. One moonlit night, after the gas lamps had been turned off, the patient caught sight of a black flat object, about four feet in diameter, sliding along the floor, near to the bed at the far end of the room.

Shaw squeezed his eyes shut, willing the presence to disappear, but when he looked back at the unusual object, he found it was still there. He knew that he was not seeing things. The shadow then eerily somehow crawled on to the bed at the end of the room, and covered the face of a another male patient.

Shaw felt ominous fear and rang a bedside bell, summoning the nurse. Before the nurse entered, the black creeping entity slipped silently off the man's face and vanished under his bed.

As the nurse tended to Shaw and attempted to calm him, she was not able to take his account of the shadow seriously. The nurse then proceeded to perform her nightly checks on her patients, and examined the man in the first bed, only to find that he had passed away.

Over the remainder of the week, the shadow being returned, and Shaw watched in terror as he saw it crawl over each bed, sometimes settling over a patient's face until the inmate of the ward woke up coughing and fighting for breath.

On Shaw's last night at the Royal, he had his closest encounter with the terrifying black liquid-like life-form. The time was half-past midnight, and he felt a sharp coldness on his foot that startled him. He looked towards the bottom of the bed and saw the black and doom ridden, shapeless object rippling as it moved across the covers towards his face. It stood up, inches from his face, as if it was ready to try and smother him, and before he lifted the blankets and let out a scream, Shaw saw two eyes slowly open up in the blackness of the entity.

Two nurses came running to Shaw's aid. They were unamused by his constant claims about the so-called shadow and they grumpily told him that they would be glad when he was discharged.

Charles Shaw's accounts were dismissed as hallucinations induced by the pain-killing medications with which he was dosed, but in the light of the similar cases we have looked at, it would seem that these sinister shadow entities have been around for quite some time.

SPOOKY SPECTRES

THE HEADLESS NUN

The following story took place in the 1970s, and I have had to change a few names and places for legal reasons. In 1977, Gregg, a used car salesman from Liverpool based in Chester, was visited by what he assumed to be a disgruntled customer as he was wielding a baseball bat. The man was an eighteen stone amateur boxer who lived in Bromborough, and he went on the rampage in Greg's used car lot, causing damage to the vehicles that amounted to over a thousand pounds. Greg rushed into his porta-cabin office, grabbed a Polaroid camera, then ran outside and took a picture of the frenzied middle-aged man as he swung the bat through windscreens and smashed the bodywork of car after car. When the man saw Greg taking his picture, it was like a red rag to a bull. With a final burst of aggression he took a swipe at him with the baseball bat, shattering the Polaroid camera. He then ran to a waiting van and the vehicle sped off.

Greg somehow managed to retrieve the snapshot from the remains of the camera, and a friend recognised the man in the photograph as an amateur Spanish pugilist named Franco. He lived in Bromborough, and was the right-hand man of one Charlie Gibbins, a notorious loan shark and small-time crook. Whenever Greg needed a bit of muscle in times of adversity, he called upon his brother-in-law Keith, a former nightclub bouncer and martial arts master who had now opted for the quieter life as a painter and decorator in Ellesmere Port. Keith wasn't scared of anyone, but couldn't afford risking his life, now that he had a wife and three children to provide for. Keith advised Greg to exact revenge on Franco via the law courts, but Greg insisted that he wanted Keith to give the Spaniard a good thrashing. It would send out a warning not to take liberties with him in future.

Keith knew that he risked being charged with assault, but reluctantly decided to go and visit Franco after Greg had accused him of losing his bottle. He visited the Bromborough pub which the Spaniard was said to frequent, and found him playing pool with a group of friends. The Spaniard was over six foot and four inches in height and brawny. Keith made no bones about telling Franco why he was there, and suggested that they should settle the score outside. Franco denied any knowledge of what had happened in Chester, at which his drunken friend suddenly made the mistake of taking a swipe at Keith with his pool cue. Keith's reflexes were second to none and he stepped back smartly, the cue tip missing his head by an inch. Keith then delivered a powerful kick at the assailant's stomach, badly winding him.

At this point the landlord stepped in and said that he didn't want any trouble in his pub, and he advised Franco to go outside with the stranger to settle the score. Franco was simmering with anger by this time and spat at Keith's foot.

"You'd better watch out, mate! You're in for a bloody good thrashing."

He then mumbled to the landlord that a friend named Charlie had unwittingly bought a highly dodgy car off a Chester used car salesman who had refused to reimburse him a thousand quid for the load of junk, hence the attack on the salesman's vehicles.

A small crowd followed Keith and Franco into the night street, but two policemen happened to be coming down the street on their beat. Keith and Franco walked off, and ended up near Dibbinsdale Bridge. Franco kept spitting and promising he'd batter Keith to within an inch of his life, and at the bridge, Keith suddenly halted, and zipped up his leather jacket. The two men turned to face one another in the moonlight, then Franco produced a hunting knife and grinned, his face contorted with menace. Keith wasn't at all fazed by the sight of the knife – his years as a bouncer had taught him how to deal with any threat. He pulled himself up to his full height and waited for the tall thug to approach, but the smile on Franco's face quickly evaporated.

Had his nerve gone? Keith wondered, then realised that Franco was not looking at him any more, but past him at something behind him. Franco then howled in fear and sped off in the other direction. Keith reflexively turned round to see what could possibly have put the wind up this seasoned fighter, to behold a sight that would haunt him for many years to come. A nun was silently gliding towards the him, and beneath her hood, where her face should have been, there was a black empty space – as if she had no head.

With the footfalls of the fleeing Spaniard echoing behind him, Keith bravely faced the sinister apparition head on, and with a bony finger it pointed at the black swirling waters below him. The ghost then leapt up and flew towards Keith, passing straight through him, and the Ellesmere Port man felt an icy chill invade his whole body. He turned quickly round but saw nothing but a shadowy shape melting back into the night. Keith was severely shaken by the incident and drove straight home, all thoughts of dealing with Franco now seeming irrelevant.

Many years later Keith discovered that Dibbinsdale Bridge in Bromborough is haunted by the ghost of a nun who went missing while walking from Birkenhead Priory to St Werburgh's in Chester in mediaeval times. There were various rumours circulating at the time that the Lord of the Manor at Bromborough had raped and murdered the nun and had somehow disposed of her body in such a way that it was never found.

Keith thought back with a shudder to the way the hooded phantom had pointed at the waters beneath the bridge, and wondered if the ghost had been trying to indicate to him where her killer had disposed of her body all those centuries ago.

THE JOYRIDERS AND THE REAPER

In the summer of 2002, Marc and Shaun – two young Liverpool men in their early twenties – took an opportunity to steal a silver Ford Puma from Penny Lane. The police were notified of the theft, and the joyriders were pursued down the M62 motorway by three patrol cars. Marc was at the wheel of the car, and as he sped down the motorway, zig-zagging between lanes, a thin summer rain began to fall. Near Junction 6 of the motorway, Marc lost control of the Puma at almost ninety miles per hour on the rain-slicked surface of Cronton Road, and collided with a metal post. Neither man had cared to wear their seat belt and both were violently catapulted through the windscreen in the crash. Shaun rolled out of control and landed in the grass, coming to a partial halt. When he opened his eyes with a groan of pain, he found that Marc was sitting next to him, gazing around, disoriented and bemused.

"It's ok," Shaun murmured to his friend, "we survived."

The two reckless young men felt light headed, and both experienced a peculiar numbness in their limbs, but they assumed the sensations were the result of shock. Shaun stood up, and gazed back at the wreckage of the Ford Puma. He turned cold. Two mangled bodies were slumped inside the wreck – their own bodies. Marc shuddered as he watched his own twitching body sprawled across the blood-splattered bonnet of the vehicle with his right foot entangled in the twisted steering wheel. Next to his body, only laying face down, was the inert body of his partner in crime, Shaun.

Down the other end of the long road, a paramedic ambulance was speeding towards them with its sirens wailing and its lights pulsating. It was followed by several police cars. Then Shaun turned, as if he sensed something approaching from his left. Before him was a very strange sight. A tall, black, cone-shaped object was apparently gliding towards the scene of the crash from the direction of Dacre's Bridge. To Shaun's still adjusting eyes, the vision looked like a man draped in a long black monk's cowl. Shaun and Marc could see that the figure was abnormally tall, at least twelve feet in height. The bizarre and decidedly sinister entity had a small head covered with a pointed black hood, and from the opening in the hood a pale face peered. As the black elongated figure grew nearer, both men could see that it was surrounded by what they could only describe as some sort of halo of darkness. This blackness formed a type of visible aura around the alarming apparition, which was silently homing in on the men.

"Run!" Marc uttered, and he tried to run away from what he felt was some Grim Reaper, but his body felt heavy, as though it was moving in slow motion. A cold darkness started to creep around him, and when he turned around, he found that Shaun was gone, but he could hear his terrible screams. The abnormally tall figure was still standing there, and he could see its hideous white face more clearly now. The features on the stark face were androgynous – they were seemingly both male and female, and the most bizarre feature of the body was its four arms and four white hands. From the bowels of the tent-like black body, Shaun was calling out and pleading for the entity to release him. Marc could hear him gasping and saying "Oh God!" over and over.

Marc could not cope with the horrendous experience he was witnessing and he turned to try and escape, but each step he attempted grew increasingly difficult to take. He was then startled by the sound of a deep and penetrating voice. It seemed to resonate from the being before him, and a strange rhythmic muffled drumming noise and odd pipe music drowned out Shaun's voice. The music sounded very sinister and unnerving, and Marc sensed that it was the very music of death. The spectral shadow of death followed Marc about that field in a cat and mouse game for an incalculable stretch of time, and the feeling of utter dread made him physically nauseous. At one point the black towering figure loomed directly over him, and when the pale face gazed down to behold the cowering young man, Marc saw that its visage looked ancient. The eyes widened with a manic expression, and its hideous mouth stretched open wide to reveal nothing but solid blackness. The sinister music was heard again, and Marc backed away, desperately asserting that he believed in God, and that only God would decide the time of his death.

The figure moved away in a circular motion and suddenly made its way off at great speed towards the motorway, until it was just a black point far off in the distance. Marc felt that the awful entity was going to wait on that motorway until there was another crash, so it could cruelly prey on the dying and the dead.

Marc experienced an odd sensation, as if he was being enveloped within some vaporous cloud, and gradually he lost consciousness. When he came to he was in hospital. The morphine he had been given had created a numbness that pervaded his entire body. He had sustained life-threatening multiple injuries yet had been revived and saved by the skills of the roadside paramedics. The experience seemed inconceivable from the perspective of his hospital bed, and Marc could not comprehend what exactly had happened. It was a week later that he learned from his girlfriend that Shaun had died in the car smash. Despite the fact that Shaun's injuries had not been half as severe as those sustained by Marc, he had not pulled through.

To this day, Marc believes that through some act of faith and willpower he somehow cheated the Grim Reaper. He has abandoned his life of petty crime, and now raises money for worthy local charities in his community.

LADY OF THE NIGHT

One Friday night in the early 1990s, a thirty-eight-year-old married father-of-three from Croxteth named Derek made his way to a social club in south Liverpool. The night's entertainment was a soul singer named Ivan Staxx. After a pleasant evening out, Derek left the club. It was around midnight, and he decided not go straight home to his wife. Instead, he impulsively went in search of a prostitute in his car, for the first time in his life.

Kerb-crawling the streets of Liverpool, Derek reached the corner of Church Road and Smithdown Place. He cautiously cruised along in his Fiesta, until he was able to make out the figure of a woman just ahead of him in the darkness. She looked to be aged about twenty, with a beautiful curvaceous figure and long blonde hair. She was provocatively dressed in thigh-length boots and mini-skirt. The young woman minced her way up Smithdown Road, and passed the Oxfam shop. Derek began to edge the car slowly over in her direction, when a police car suddenly came from the other direction. Derek panicked. If the police stopped him, what reasons could he possibly give for being in the area? his guilty conscience asked.

Derek accelerated quickly and overtook the girl he believed to be a prostitute, and turned down a side street, glancing back at her as he did so. He was very surprised when he caught sight of the girl's face, because she looked like a slightly older version of the girl who once babysat for him several years ago.

"Jayne," he said softly to himself as he carefully and silently drove over the traffic-calming humps of the side street. He heard the police car pass on by. He sighed with relief that he had gone unnoticed.

He felt fondness at the recollection of Jayne. Derek had developed a liking for her, when she was just seventeen. She had left the neighbourhood when her family moved to the Sefton Park area a few years back and Derek's contact with her had ceased. A rather vain and self-deluding man, Derek had convinced himself that Jayne had always had an unspoken liking for him. He wondered what on earth she was doing out at this hour, as it was almost one o'clock in the morning. She didn't appear to be carrying a handbag, and girls rarely went out without something to carry their make-up and accessories in, reasoned Derek. Jayne was perhaps walking the streets for some immoral purpose.

Derek edged his Ford Fiesta out of another side street and continued along Smithdown Road, and at that precise moment, he caught another fleeting glance of Jayne turning the corner, which would take her on to Arundel Avenue. Derek quickly turned his vehicle around the corner and saw the girl walking down the right side of the avenue. He killed the speed of his vehicle, and felt his mouth dry up. His heart was pounding. What should he do to attract her attention, he asked himself, his mind fluttering passionately like that of a teenage boy. He wound down the window, and watched her walking along with a sensual gait, her platinum blonde hair flowing in the night breeze.

Derek flashed his lights to high beam for a moment, in an effort to make the girl turn that lovely head, but she just kept on walking.

"Hey!" Derek shouted out.

He hoped it was his former babysitter, but then again, if it wasn't, he was sure that the female ahead of him was a lady of the night.

Still she did not respond, and Derek shouted to her twice more, to no avail. He became annoyed, thinking that the girl was childishly playing hard-to-get. Unamused by this possibility, he was about to shout at the girl again when she turned abruptly and walked straight through a solid brick wall. Derek could not believe what he witnessed. He was so shocked, he narrowly missed a rubbish skip at the road side and screeched his car to a stammering halt.

Derek gazed at the redbrick wall, in shock. He cursed under his breath and squinted more closely at the wall. No, there were definitely no doorways there. There were no passageways at all. Before him was simply just a solid wall, and that girl had passed through it as if it wasn't there. She must have been a ghost, assumed Derek, his mind cluttered with frantic fears which overwhelmed him with a strange and instinctive feeling that the young woman would come back out from that wall very soon. He drove off hastily and forced as much distance as he could between himself and that sinister wall.

Derek turned up Hartington Road, and noticed a cemetery to his right. "Jesus," he said out loud to himself, as he realised that the redbrick wall the girl had just vanished through formed part of the back wall of the cemetery. He was reluctant to glance into the shadows of the vast graveyard in case he saw the girl, and so he drove off at high speed, all the way home.

That night he slipped into the bed where his wife Joanne was lightly sleeping. She was awakened by his cold body invading the warmth beneath the sheets.

"Where have you been?" she muttered sleepily.

"I met an old friend at the social club, and I had to give him a lift home to Toxteth," Derek lied.

He sank back into the pillows, holding Joanne close in the darkness, thinking about the ghost going through that wall. He was coated in a cold sweat and his heart was palpitating.

"What's wrong?"

Joanne's unfathomable female intuition homed in on her husband's anxiety. She could sense something was worrying him, even though she couldn't even see his face.

Derek spoke vaguely about seeing a blonde woman aged about twenty walk through the wall of a cemetery on Arundel Avenue, as he drove home. After a pause, he added that the apparition had resembled their former babysitter, Jayne.

Joanne sat up, then reached out and turned on the bedside lamp. In fourteen years of marriage, she had long learned the art of lie-detection as far as her husband was concerned, and she knew he was telling the truth about the ghost, even though she was oblivious to the real circumstances leading up to the supernatural incident. She rubbed her husband's back to try and calm him down. She did not speak for a few moments.

"Jayne had leukaemia, the last I heard," she sighed sympathetically as she turned off the light and cuddled up to her husband.

On the following day, Joanne was on the telephone to a friend who lived close to Jayne's family in Sefton Park. She discovered that the babysitter had died just a year before from her condition. She had been buried in Toxteth Park Cemetery.

This strange story doesn't end there. A month later, Derek toyed with the idea of kerb-crawling again, only this time he realised that he did not want to actually pick up a lady of the night; he merely got a kick out of cruising in red light areas. He was driving down Upper Parliament Street, when a girl walked out in front of his car. It was Jayne. There was no doubt about it. He slammed on the brakes and narrowly missed the apparition, and in the brief moment he saw the ghost's face, he noted the dark sunken eyes and pallid complexion.

On this occasion, events took an even more chilling turn, because the ghostly girl somehow followed Derek across Toxteth and Aigburth. He drove down side streets and residential leafy lanes, and kept catching a glimpse of the blonde phantom, always heading in his direction. When he reached his home he was horrified to see a blonde head through the frosted glass of the front door. The door opened and Derek was relieved to see that Joanne's friend, Melanie, was the blonde in his house. She had been keeping Joanne company until Derek returned from his purported night out at the cinema.

Derek was so affected by the ghost of Jayne, he ended up confessing to his sordid kerb-crawling, and eventually changed his ways. To date, Derek has not seen the ghost again, but I have received many reports of the spectral lady of the night, who roams the streets of Liverpool after dark, often being mistaken as a flesh and blood girl.

AN INVISIBLE INTRUDER

It is hard to categorise the following peculiar incident, which was related to me by two individual readers. In August 1970, Sandra and Michelle, two fourteen-year-old girls from Everton, went to stay with Sandra's Aunt Shelley, an outlandish woman who was regarded as something of a black sheep by her three sisters. Sandra's mum would often remark that Shelley was forty going on twenty; that she wore too much make up and dressed inappropriately for her age, wearing mini skirts and skimpy tops. Sandra hadn't seen her wayward aunt since she was nine, and her only recollection of her was that Shelley had been a generous and good humoured woman who was always fun to be around. Sandra had pestered her mum for years, asking if she could go and visit Shelley and even stay over at her house, and now her mother had acquiesced at last.

Shelley had married and divorced three times, and was currently living with a man with the unusual name of Drake Richardson. As soon as Sandra and Michelle got off the bus, they made their way to the house on Windsor Street in Toxteth. Standing before the address they had been given, they were faced with a decaying, three-floored Victorian building. The exterior appeared neglected, and only partly remaining was a patchy layer of old and flaking paint. The girls looked at each other, before stepping nearer to the house. Sandra immediately spotted her extrovert aunt standing in the doorway with a cigarette in her smiling mouth. Her eyes followed the movements of a muscular young man across the road who was innocently washing his car.

Michelle smirked when she saw her friend's auntie. She looked exactly as she had imagined her to. The permed head of orange curly hair, the layer of pale foundation that masked her face, the heavy panda mascara, the diaphanous bra-like top and the infamous mini skirt that looked at least a size too small.

"Auntie Shelley," Sandra said with a rather meek tone. She blushed for some reason.

Shelley had just stomped the sole of her fluffy pink slipper on the last end of her cigarette. As she looked back up in response to the voice she half recognised, her expression dropped from one of pleasant flirtation to one of hostility. She squinted her eyes at Sandra. Her unwelcoming glances skimmed over her and looked her up and down, before also repeating the process Michelle.

"What was that, love?" Her tone was neither welcoming nor hostile.

"It's me, Sandra; Maureen's girl," Sandra replied, hoping her aunt hadn't disowned her because of some family feud.

The mascara coated eyelashes flickered. The pencilled-in Vulcan eyebrows lifted as Shelley started to recognise the face.

"Oh my God!" Shelley clamped her hand, laden with gold rings, against her chest, and then swore under her breath.

A bald man, aged about fifty, with patches of blonde hair on each side of his head emerged from the hall and now joined them on the front step. He wore a string vest and a pair of bottle-green flared trousers.

"What's up, babe?" he said, noticing that Shelley was heartily embracing a young girl. He looked at the girls with a decidedly lustful leer, his gaze falling particularly upon Michelle, who felt very uncomfortable receiving the man's seemingly lecherous interest.

Shelley turned around to face him.

"It's me favourite niece, our Maureen's girl, Sandra!" she exclaimed with great excitement.

Sandra smiled shyly at the man, who, judging by his greatly receded hair and dirty string vest, was the Drake her disapproving mother had told her about.

"Come on in girls!" Shelley threw her arms around both teenagers' necks and led them indoors, where an old record player was struggling to blare out 'Wandrin' Star' by Lee Marvin.

Drake scuttled past the girls and leant to turn down the volume on the record player. He turned back to face them, assessing them from head to toe once again. His expression was still as seedy as it had seemed on their introduction.

Shelley broke into the awkward moment as she looked in the fridge, and uttered a subdued profanity.

"We're out of lemmo," she muttered. "Drake, could you go to Mrs Ali's shop and get a few bottles of pop and some sweets for these two?"

Drake obeyed and set off to the shop without hesitation. During his absence the girls chatted excitedly. Sandra could not resist asking about Drake. Shelley took the chance to confess to Sandra and Michelle that she was actually thinking of ending the relationship.

"Why?" Sandra asked. It was clear that Drake had made her a little uncomfortable, but she was concerned that there was more to him than met the eye.

"He's weird." Shelley quickly replied. "I've known him about six months, and he won't tell me if he's married, single, divorced or anything. He's as deep as the ocean, and he's spooky as well!"

"Spooky?" her niece queried, drawn into the conversation with increasing curiosity.

"Oh nothing ..." Shelley said quietly.

She made a concerted effort to then change the conversation on to reminiscences about the days when she used to take Sandra over to New Brighton and the caravan site at Betws-y-Coed they had visited on a family holiday years ago.

Shelley was pleased that the girls had decided to spend some time with her. That evening, she left them sitting watching television, while she went upstairs to run a bath, this meant they were alone with Drake.

As soon as Shelley left the room, Drake got up out of his armchair and turned down the volume on the television. He proceeded to strike up a conversation with the girls, who were cautiously glancing at each other. He probed the girls by asking them uncomfortable questions about their personal lives. Were they dating? he wanted to know. Did they intend to have kids before marriage? Did they fancy any boys at school?

Sandra and Michelle edged closer together on the sofa. The loathsome Drake made their flesh crawl with his sleazy and intrusive talk. Shelley's remark about him being weird was ringing in both of the girl's ears as they tried not to appear impolite.

"This place has a ghost. Did Shelley tell you that?" he said to Sandra. She shook her head.

"No one's seen him, like. He's invisible, but you can hear him on the stairs during the night."

Drake smirked and seemed to relish the wide-eyed fear on the girls' young faces.

"Who is he?" Michelle asked timidly.

"Nobody knows," Drake told her, "but he likes the women. He slapped your Aunt Shelley's behind the other night."

The girls shuddered, and were extremely relieved when Shelley made her way back downstairs, this time draped in her flimsy golden bathrobe and flip-flops.

Sandra and Michelle could not hold back their concern and they immediately asked Shelley if the ghost was real and whether it had really slapped her. Shelley turned to Drake with a disapproving glare on her face. She accused him of being irresponsible for frightening her guests with such unsettling ghost stories, but her eyes betrayed her dismissal, she looked unsettled at the mention of the spectre.

At around midnight, the girls grew weary and went to Shelley's spare bedroom, where they shared an old and dusty double bed. Shelley settled them in and said goodnight to them, while Drake went into the bathroom. He said he wanted to bathe for a while before retiring because it was such a hot night.

Within half an hour, the girls were in bed, unsuccessfully attempting to stifle their giggling because they could hear Shelley snoring. Unable to sleep from giddiness, the girls put on the bedside lamp. Michelle lay reading her *Jackie* Magazine in the lamplight, as Sandra sat painting her toenails a dark shade of purple.

All of a sudden, Sandra threw up her hand and yelped. The nail polish bottle and its built-in brush went flying across the room. She moved away quickly.

Michelle looked up, startled by the sudden shriek and the clunk of the nail polish bottle hitting the wall.

"Something just touched my hair!" Sandra shrieked.

She dashed back over to the bed and felt the spot where she had definitely been stroked on the head by something which had lifted a lock of her blonde hair.

Michelle got into the bed and pulled the edge of the quilt up to her eyes.

Sandra wriggled down under the covers as well, and listened to the tense silence.

"Oh!" Michelle shouted, and ducked under the blankets.

She whispered to Sandra that she had just felt someone sit on her foot at the end of the bed.

The girls grew so scared that they hurried out of the room. Standing there alone on the dark landing, Sandra tapped on the bedroom door from which her aunt's snoring was reverberating, but the woman couldn't be roused from her obviously deep sleep. They edged nervously into the room, but knew that waking her was a lost cause when Michelle pointed out the small brown medicine bottle on the bedside cabinet. The label read Diazepam, Shelley had taken some sleeping pills.

The girls decided that their last resort was Drake, so they went off in search of him. They hunted around the house for him, first trying the bathroom. There they discovered a full bath, and beside the bath and folded neatly on a chair, were Drake's clothes. There was absolutely no sign of the man himself.

Sandra and Michelle crept downstairs and sat in the unlit lounge, still shaken by the ghostly encounter in the bedroom. They jumped as they detected creaks and sounds on the stairs, and remembered what Drake had told them about the sinister ghost earlier in the evening. The teenagers were so scared, they refused to budge from the lounge, until 2.30am, when Sandra went into the kitchen to make something to eat. She found that there was virtually no food in the fridge or the larder, so she decided to boil a couple of eggs and toast some bread. The food seemed a comfort in the uncomfortable dreariness of the somewhat deserted house.

Michelle followed her friend into the kitchen. She was very shaken as she explained nervously that she had just seen something moving about in the lounge out of the corner of her eye. The girls stood stock still in the kitchen, wishing they were safely back in their own homes. Looking out of the window, the girls felt very detached indeed from the safety for their homes. Michelle leant further into the glass and drew a circle in the condensation, the tiniest of distractions helping to keep her calm.

All of a sudden, Sandra yelled out and spun around. She was convinced that she had felt the hot and heavy breath of a person right behind her, she could not explain it but was sure that there had been a nibbling sensation at her ear lobe. She shook her head and ruffled her hair as if shaking off the invisible intrusion. Michelle was standing near the window, and before their very eyes, upon the condensation of the pane where she had drawn a circle with her fingertip, two marks for eyes and a smiley mouth slowly appeared in that circle. Goose pimples shot up on Michelle's arms. She stood there totally immobilised as she watched the invisible sketcher at work. As Michelle screamed, Sandra grabbed the handle of the pan in which she was boiling the eggs, and hurled its contents at the window, where the ghost was currently active.

A distinctive male voice let out an agonised scream as the boiling water splashed upon its invisible body. The girls dashed out of the kitchen and Michelle felt the presence of something unseen knock against her arm as she fled. Sandra and Michelle bounded up the stairs and back towards their bedroom. They heard the voice of a man who seemed to be in intense pain cursing them with obscene language. In the bedroom, the girls struggled to drag a cabinet in front of the door in an attempt to bar the angry ghost's entry. As the night dragged on, the girls sensed that the commotion and activity seemed to be dying down. Exhausted by the distressing night, they both fell into a light sleep.

Early on the following morning they dashed into Shelley's bedroom and vigorously shook her awake. They told her about their terrifying experience at the hands of the invisible assailant, but Shelley was too groggy to take it in.

However, when Shelley and the girls went downstairs, they saw that Drake's left arm and wrist were swathed in bandages. He avoided eye contact with Shelley as he muttered that he had accidentally scalded himself in the kitchen with a pan of boiling water. Sandra glanced at Michelle, and knew that she was thinking the same thing. Had Drake somehow been the intrusive ghost who they had scalded in the early hours of the morning?

The girls were convinced that the very notion was impossible, yet the only explanation available seemed to be that Drake was somehow able to make himself invisible. Whether it was actual invisibility or whether he had used some sort of hypnotism was never established.

Sandra and Michelle left the house and went home that day, with no intentions of returning for a repeat performance! Shelley's suspicions that there was something very strange about Drake were now confirmed and so she told him to pack his bags.

For years, Sandra and Michelle were haunted by their bizarre and inexplicable experiences at the old house in Windsor Street.

THE OLD LADY OF ALLERTON ROAD

Just why ghosts continue to haunt the places they frequented while they were in a flesh and blood body is anyone's guess. I think in cases where a person dies before his or her time, perhaps violently, their ghost may return, either to seek justice, or because of unfinished business in its life. The bond of love is very powerful, and seems to easily transcend the barrier of death. The bond of love between parents, grandparents and children, or between two people, can help to explain why some people come back from the other side. A mother or father would certainly return in some capacity from the afterlife to appear to their children, or at least give a sign to reassure their offspring that they are still around. Some people lose loved ones and never receive the slightest sign from them – but in many cases the signs are there and go unnoticed.

I have received reports that ghosts are being seen on Liverpool's streets going through the same routines they carried out when they were on the earthly plane. A good example of this type of ghost is the apparition of an elderly woman who walks up Allerton Road. She wears a long beige coat, black, heeled shoes, and a box hat with a diaphanous veil which covers her pale wrinkled face. This ghost has been reported to me many times, and here are just a few of these reports.

A thirty-eight-year-old teacher named Jayne, of Swanside, was walking up Allerton Road at noon one day in August 2001 with her eight-year-old daughter, Sophie. It was raining quite hard, and mother and daughter were hurrying towards the bank. Several minutes later,

Jayne and Sophie left the bank and proceeded along Allerton Road in the downpour under an umbrella. Jayne intended to walk to the nearby supermarket, Tescos, which is located on Mather Avenue. Instead of holding her mother's hand, Sophie straggled behind, and when Jayne turned, she thought she could hear footsteps walking behind her, quite near to Sophie, who was walking silently in her trainers. Jayne walked on and gradually became aware of an old woman in a long beige coat walking along with her and Sophie, but, overwhelmed by the sheets of rain hammering down, the teacher hardly took any notice of the elderly person accompanying them.

However, as Jayne and Sophie walked on to the central reservation on Rose Lane and waited for the lights of the pelican crossing to change, the old woman stood next to them. Sophie smiled up at the lady. "Hello," she said, looking up and shrugging at the awful weather. The elderly woman just looked right through the little girl – and then vanished into thin air. Jayne was also a witness to the startling vanishing act. Sophie became hysterical, and was naturally very shaken by the supernatural incident. It was two weeks before the child would go up to her bedroom on her own. Jayne's response to the occurrence was one of intrigue. She was baffled, and wrote to me to see if I had heard of the mysterious apparition.

Indeed the ghost has been seen by many people over the years, including a man named Simon who lives on Wembley Road, in the Allerton district. Simon left Domino's newsagents on Allerton Road one Friday afternoon in 2002, and walked behind a woman in an angular-looking hat of some sort and a long, pale, creamy-brown woollen coat.

As Simon was about to pass the woman, she disappeared in an instant, leaving him stunned. Just weeks after this, a woman from nearby Green Lane saw the same seemingly solid-looking old lady before witnessing her rapid dematerialisation, near to Allerton Library.

Just why this old lady's ghost is seen, always walking along Allerton Road, is a mystery. Did something traumatic once happen to her on that stretch of road? Perhaps she passed away or was even knocked down by a car in that area, and the release of emotional energy left some sort of holographic image behind, imprinted in space and time. It is all conjecture of course, but the next time you travel down Allerton Road, keep a look out for the lady with the box hat and the veil ...

OTHER SIMILAR TITLES

Haunted Cheshire	Tom Slemen	£5.99
Haunted Liverpool 1	Tom Slemen	£5.99
Haunted Liverpool 2	Tom Slemen	£5.99
Haunted Liverpool 3	Tom Slemen	£5.99
Haunted Liverpool 4	Tom Slemen	£5.99
Haunted Liverpool 5	Tom Slemen	£5.99
Haunted Liverpool 6	Tom Slemen	£5.99
Haunted Liverpool 7	Tom Slemen	£5.99
Haunted Liverpool 8	Tom Slemen	£5.99
Haunted Liverpool 9	Tom Slemen	£5.99
Haunted Liverpool 10	Tom Slemen	£5.99
Haunted Wirral	Tom Slemen	£5.99
Wicked Liverpool	Tom Slemen	£5.99
Mysterious World	Tom Slemen	£5.99
Haunted Liverpool 1 Audio Book, read by	Tom Slemen	£8.99
A Different Sky, UFOs in Merseyside	Tony Eccles	£5.99

Available from all good bookshops.

If you have had a paranormal encounter or a supernatural experience,
you can contact Tom Slemen:

Tom Slemen
c/o The Bluecoat Press
19 Rodney Street
Liverpool L1 9EF

All correspondence will be answered.